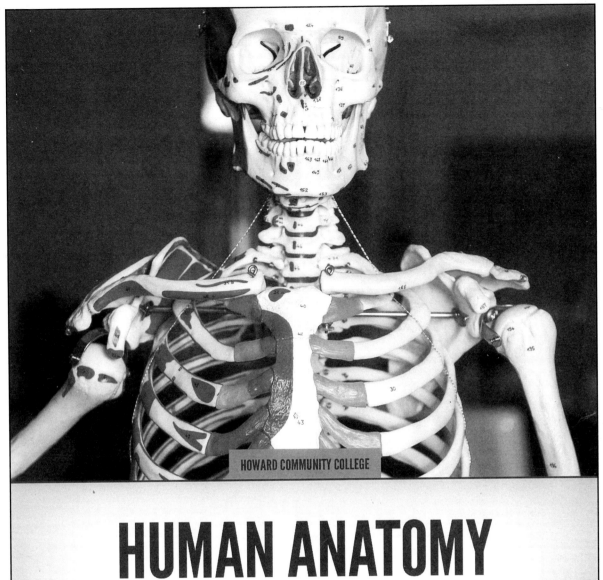

HOWARD COMMUNITY COLLEGE

HUMAN ANATOMY AND PHYSIOLOGY I

LABORATORY MANUAL, SECOND EDITION

bluedoor

flexible & affordable learning solutions

Chief Executive Officer: Jon K. Earl

President, College: Lucas Tomasso
President, Private Sector: Dawn Earl
Regional Manager: Greg Bartell

Print Solutions Manager: Connie Dayton
Digital Solutions Manager: Amber Wahl
Developmental & Production Coordinator: Rhiannon Nelson
Production Manager: Dan Woods
Production Manager: Erica Rieck
Project Manager: Peggy Li
Production Assistant: Ben Sweeney
Production Assistant: Stephanie Larson

Consulting Editors: Bruce D. Wingerd, M.S.
                     Suzanne S. Frucht, Ph.D.
                     Anna M. Kats, M.S., Florida Atlantic University
                     Michelle F. Cavallo, M.S., Florida Atlantic University
                     John F. Wiginton, Ph.D., University of Mississippi
                     Stephanie R. Dillon, Ph.D., Florida State University

Cover Design: Dan Woods

ISBN-13: 978-1-59984-893-8

© 2015 Howard Community College.

© Cover image by Howard Community College.

Published by bluedoor, LLC
              10949 Bren Road East
              Minneapolis, MN 55343-9613
              800-979-1624
              www.bluedoorpublishing.com

Printed in the United States of America.
10 9 8 7 6 5 4 3 2 1

PREFACE TO BIOL 203 LAB STUDENTS

The BIOL 203 laboratory program is designed to provide a variety of active experiences that will lead to a better understanding of the body systems studied in this course. The weekly lab exercises include microscopy, dissection and experiments.

The lab manual has been designed to provide an organized, easy to use tool to assist the student as they learn about the laboratory aspects of human anatomy and physiology.

Each lab exercise is organized into the following components:

Objectives: The objectives state exactly what students are responsible for knowing on laboratory examinations.

Introduction: This section provides a brief discussion of the lab exercises that will be performed during that lab period.

Materials: The materials list indicates what equipment should be present at the workbench and what equipment is available in the room to be shared by students. It is a good idea to have all of the equipment that you need at your bench before you begin an activity.

Activities: The weekly program is broken down into a number of activities that correspond to the objectives. The activities may include the following sections:

Resources: You must bring your textbook (Human Anatomy and Physiology, 9th edition, Elaine Marieb) to the lab each week. Each activity may reference text and/or illustrations the text book.

Directions: A concise procedure for completing the activity.

Tips: Helpful hints for completing the activity more effectively and successfully

Checklist: Use this to make sure that you have completed all of your work before you leave.

Worksheet: The worksheet has two sections:

Lab worksheets: This section is to be completed during the lab period.

Post lab worksheets: This section is to help you to prepare for the following week's lab quiz. It need not be handed in for grading, unless your lab instructor advises otherwise.

BIOL 203 LAB GUIDELINES

A. Procedures

1. Attire

You are encouraged to wear comfortable clothing when attending the lab. You will be working with a variety of specimens and chemicals so you may want to bring a lab coat or an old shirt to protect your clothing. You may not wear open-toed shoes in the lab. Safety glasses or goggles may be required during some procedures. The use of contact lenses is discouraged. **No open-toed shoes, sandals, or flip flops are permitted to be worn in the lab!**

2. Attendance

Attendance at all lab sessions is mandatory. If an emergency situation arises which prevents you from attending, you must contact your lab instructor within 24 hours of your scheduled lab session. You will be asked to provide a documented excuse for your absence. You will not be permitted to make up a missed lab for any other reason such as doctor's appointments, work schedule conflicts, running errands etc. Lab practicals must be taken during your regularly scheduled lab period.

All lab quizzes are given during the first 15 minutes of the lab period. If you arrive after the quiz has begun you will not be given additional time to complete the quiz.

Procedures to follow if you miss a lab:

We understand that there are rare, emergency situations that might prevent you from attending your regularly-scheduled lab period. You are only permitted two make-up lab sessions during the semester. You must follow this procedure to arrange for a make-up lab:

a. You must contact your lab instructor within 24 hours of your regularly-scheduled lab period. Your lab instructor will provide you with information about an alternative lab section and you will be responsible for contacting the lab instructor for that session to make arrangements to attend.

b. You must obtain the signature of the lab instructor who taught the make-up session on your worksheet before you leave the lab.

c. The signed worksheet must be submitted to your lab instructor at the beginning of the next regularly-scheduled lab session.

3. Lab Materials

Lab equipment and materials are costly and delicate. It is your responsibility to maintain all lab materials in good condition. Please alert your lab instructor if materials are missing or if equipment is broken. If you need something, please ask for it. You are responsible for leaving your workbench in a clean and orderly state, and for returning materials to a designated location.

4. Safety

Proper behavior in the laboratory will ensure your safety and the safety of those around you. *Children are not permitted in the lab under any circumstances.* General safety guidelines are presented on page vi. More specific safety procedures will be presented by the lab instructors on an as-needed basis each week. Failure to adhere to safety guidelines will result in your removal from the laboratory.

5. Academic Honesty

Academic honesty, as stated in the HCC Student Handbook, is required of all students:

"Academic Honesty means the use of one's own thoughts and materials in the writing of papers, taking of tests, and other classroom-related activities. Any student intentionally aiding another student in any infraction of the Academic Honesty Policy is considered equally guilty.

Students are expected to give full credit for the borrowing of others' words or ideas. Intentional or unintentional use of another's words or ideas without acknowledging this use constitutes plagiarism:

- The duplication of an author's words without quotation marks and accurate references or footnotes.

- The duplication of author's words or phrases with footnotes or accurate references but without quotation marks.

- The use of an author's ideas in paraphrase without accurate references or footnotes.

- Submitting a paper in which exact words are merely rearranged even though footnoted.

Misrepresentation is the submission of materials for evaluation that are not the student's own.

Unauthorized use of notes or another individual's materials, copying, using another individual's materials, or unauthorized prior knowledge of the contents of tests, quizzes or other assessment instruments shall be considered a violation of the Academic Honesty Policy."

Reference: HCC 2013-2014 Catalogue, pages 43-44

6. Responsibilities

Preparation: Read the lab exercise in advance. Have questions ready for the lab instructor.

During the lab period: Perform the activities included in the lab manual. Complete the Lab Activities portion of the Worksheet. Judicious use of your lab time will reduce the amount of time that you have to spend on your own to learn the material.

After the lab period: Continue to review the lab material in preparation for the following week's quiz and for the lab practicals.

7. Late Assignments

All assignments will be assessed a 3-point per day late fee. No assignments will be accepted after 1 week.

8. Assignment Submission

All written assignments are required to be submitted through the course Canvas site. Your instructor will give specific instructions accordingly.

B. Grading

1. Lab Worksheets

These worksheets are designed to help students master the concepts introduced each week in the laboratory. The exercises should be completed individually and are due at the designated time. Answers to the questions can generally be found in the lab manual and/or in the textbook.

2. Weekly Quizzes   100 points

Weekly quizzes will be given each week (except weeks 1, 6, 7 and 14). The quiz covers the prior week's lab material.

3. Assignments   25 points

Three written assignments are given.

4. Lab Report   25 points

One written lab report is required during the semester. Guidelines for writing the report will be distributed.

5. Lab Practicals   200 points

Comprehensive lab exams will be administered during the 6th and the 14th weeks of the semester. Questions will be based on all lab objectives listed in your lab manual. The format for these exams will be discussed by your lab instructor during the semester. Correct spelling of all terms is required. Deductions are made for incorrect spelling. Each incorrect spelling carries a quarter-point deduction. You are required to take your lab practical during your assigned lab period. **Rare** exceptions may be made in the event of a documented emergency and at the discretion of the lab instructor.

If you miss the lab practical for a documented emergency situation you will be given an electronic make-up practical.

> In order to receive a passing grade in BIOL 203 you must achieve an average of 60% or better in *both* the lecture and the lab. You must receive at least 210 points to pass lab and lecture.

C. Lab schedule

Week	Lab Topic	Evaluation Due	Point Value
1	Introduction to Anatomic Terminology	Worksheet Wk 1	
2	Human Cells/Histology: Epithelial tissue	Quiz lab 1 Worksheet Wk 2	10
3	Histology: Connective Tissue	Quiz lab 2 Worksheet Wk 3	10
4	The Skeletal System	Quiz lab 3	10
5	The Skeletal System	Quiz lab 4 Worksheet Wk 4&5	10
6	**Lab Practical #1**	Exam	100
7	The Muscular System — Human	Worksheet Wk 7 Lab assignment 1	5
8	The Muscular System -Cat	Quiz lab 7 Worksheet Wk 8 Lab assignment 2	10 10
9	The Nervous System — Histology/Brain	Quiz lab 7&8 Worksheet Wk 9 Lab assignment 3	10 10
10	Cranial Nerves	Quiz lab 9 Worksheet Wk 10	10
11	The Peripheral Nervous System	Quiz lab 10 Worksheet Wk 11	10
12	The Special Senses	Quiz lab 11 Worksheet Wk 12 Lab report	10 25
13	The Integumentary System	Quiz lab 12 Worksheet Wk 13	10
14	**Lab Practical #2**	Exam	100
		Total*	**350**

* Note: The lowest quiz score (10 points) will dropped and the highest quiz score will be substituted for the dropped score. Missed quizzes/assignments cannot be made up. You will receive a zero for any missed quiz.

LABORATORY SAFETY PROCEDURES

1. Locate the following safety equipment: fire extinguisher, chemical shower, eye wash station, first aid kit and broken glass containers. Know how to use them.

2. Notify your lab instructor immediately after any injury (no matter how small), equipment failure or spill.

3. Know the building evacuation procedures.

4. Never eat, drink, smoke, apply cosmetics or handle contact lenses while in the laboratory. You are advised to wear eye glasses instead of contact lenses.

5. Students who are pregnant, have allergies, or have other medical conditions that require precautions should notify their lab instructor immediately.

6. Read labels and safety warnings carefully.

7. Do not use any equipment unless you are trained and approved as a user by your lab instructor.

8. Wear protective safety glasses when dissecting and working with hazardous materials and/or equipment.

9. Wear gloves when using any hazardous or toxic agent.

10. Sandals, open-toed shoes, or flip flops are not permitted to be worn in the lab at any time.

11. Long hair and loose clothes should be restrained. Remove dangling jewelry.

12. Keep the work area and floor clear of all materials except those needed for your work. Extra books, purses, etc. should be kept in designated areas (drawers are usually available).

13. Students are responsible for the proper disposal of used material in appropriate containers.

14. If a piece of equipment fails while being used, report it immediately to your lab instructor. Never try to fix the problem yourself because you could harm yourself and others.

15. Perform only those experiments authorized by the instructor. Never do anything in the laboratory that is not called for in the laboratory procedures or by your instructor. Carefully follow all instructions, both written and oral. Unauthorized experiments are prohibited.

16. Clean up your work area before leaving.

17. Wash hands before leaving the lab.

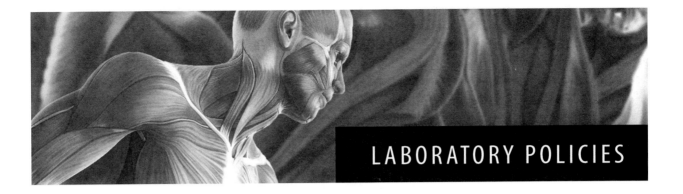

BIOLOGY 203 LABORATORY POLICIES

1. You must attend the lab in which you are registered

2. It is expected that you will arrive to lab on time. Lab quizzes will start promptly at the beginning of lab. The time allotted for quizzes is 15 minutes. If you arrive late you will not be given additional time to complete the quiz. If you arrive after the quiz has been administered you will not be able to take the quiz at a later time.

3. In order to receive credit for a lab worksheet you must do the work in lab. Labs are scheduled for a three-hour period. You must stay for the entire three-hour scheduled lab period. If you leave after the quiz has been administered, you will not be given credit for your quiz grade.

4. Attendance at all lab sessions is mandatory. If an **emergency** situation arises which prevents you from attending, you must contact your lab instructor within 24 hours of your scheduled lab session. You will be asked to provide a documented excuse for your absence. You will not be permitted to make up a missed lab for reasons such as a regularly-scheduled doctor's appointment, work schedule conflicts, running errands, etc.

5. You must follow this procedure to arrange for a make-up lab:

    a. You must contact your lab instructor within 24 hours of your regularly-scheduled lab period. Your lab instructor will provide you with information about an alternative lab section and you will be responsible for contacting the lab instructor via email for that session to make arrangements to attend. You must copy your regular lab instructor on the email requesting to attend the make-up lab.

    b. You must obtain the signature of the lab instructor who taught the make-up session on your worksheet before you leave the lab. Also have them date the lab worksheet under their signature.

    c. The signed worksheet must be submitted to your lab instructor at the beginning of the next regularly-scheduled lab session.

6. You cannot attend more than 2 make-up labs during the semester.

7. If you miss a lab, and do not attend a make-up session, you will not be given credit for the lab, i.e., lab assignments, quiz, and/or lab report. There are no opportunities for make-up quizzes as a result of missing a lab.

8. Please note that if you do not attend the cranial nerve testing lab you will **not** be permitted to turn in a lab report and will lose the 25 points.

9. If you miss lab it is your responsibility to get any missed notes, announcements, handouts, etc.

10. If you miss your regularly-scheduled lab practical you will not be permitted to take it with another section. You must contact your lab instructor within 24 hours of the missed lab practical. If you have a valid documented excuse, you will be given an electronic version that must be taken within the 48 hour period after your regularly-scheduled lab session. For example, if your lab session meets on Tuesday at 2pm you must complete the make-up lab practical by Thursday at 3pm. There will be no exceptions to this rule. Only emergency circumstances **that are documented** will be accepted for taking the make-up practical.

11. All late assignments will be assessed a 3-point per day late fee. For example, if an assignment or lab worksheet is due on a Monday and handed in on Tuesday 3 points will be deducted automatically. No late assignments will be accepted after 1 week.

12. Lab reports must have an originality score of 25% or less (turnitin.com score) in order to be accepted for grading. This score must be obtained on or before the due date. If the originality score is above 25% under no circumstances will the report be accepted for grading, i.e. you will receive a zero for the report. Please ask your lab instructor for specifics on this policy.

13. BIOL 203 lab strictly adheres to the HCC academic honesty policies. Review the academic honesty policies in the HCC catalogue. Stated penalties for failure to abide by the policies will be followed.

BIOL 203 STUDENT INFORMATION

Student name: _____

Contact information: Cell phone: _____ _____

Home phone: _____ _____

Email: _____

Lecture instructor: _____ _____

Lecture day/time: _____ _____

1. Do you have any specific interests in anatomy and physiology?

2. What is your major or career goal (pre-nursing, pre-med, pre-pharmacology, etc.)?

3. Do you have any concerns about this lab?

4. Please read and sign the following statement:

I have read the BIOL 203 lab guidelines and policies. I understand them and agree to comply with them. I understand that failure to comply with the guidelines and policies will result in implementation of policies that may adversely affect my lab grade and final course grade.

_____   _____   _____

Printed name   Signature   Date

TABLE OF CONTENTS

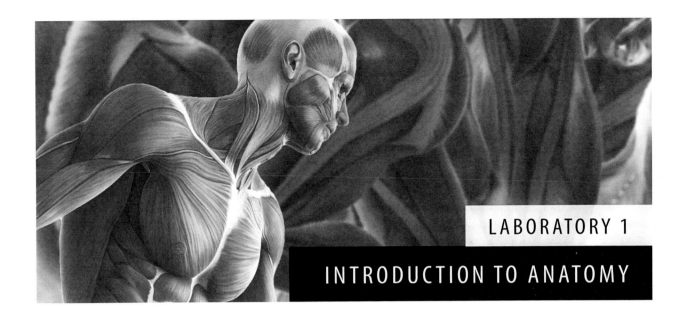

OBJECTIVES

1. Describe anatomical position for both bipeds and quadripeds, and apply anatomic terminology to both human and animal models. For specific terms see activity 1.

2. Locate the following body planes using models and specimens: sagittal (midsagittal, parasagittal), frontal (coronal), transverse (cross-section).

3. Locate, identify, and be able to state which organs are located in the following body cavities and abdominopelvic regions using models and specimens:

   a. Cavities: ventral (thoracic, abdominal, pelvic); dorsal (cranial, spinal).

   b. Abdominopelvic regions: epigastric, umbilical, hypogastric, right/left hypochondriac, right/left lumbar, right/left iliac.

4. Identify the following body systems, their major organs, and indicate the functions of each system:

Integumentary	Cardiovascular	Reproductive
Nervous	Skeletal	Lymphatic
Muscular	Endocrine	Respiratory
Digestive	Urinary	

5. Properly dissect a rat and identify structures listed in lab activity 5.

INTRODUCTION

Anatomy deals with the study of the structure of different body parts and their relationship to one another. Physiology is the study of how these body parts work together (how they function together). Learning anatomy is comparable to learning a new language where different terminologies are used in reference to the body parts and their relationship to each other. This use of anatomical terminology helps to prevent confusion and leads to a better-understood universal language.

The initial reference point is a standard body position called anatomical position. In this position the body is erect and facing forward, the feet are slightly apart, and the upper appendages are hanging at the side with palms facing forwards. One has to clearly understand that the different directional terms used in anatomy are <u>always</u> applied in relation to the standard anatomical position and not to the actual position of the person or the body or the organ being viewed.

The two very basic divisions of our body are the axial and appendicular portions. The axial portion includes the head, neck and trunk. The appendicular portion is made up of appendages (limbs) that are attached to the axis.

In order to study the body or an organ (internal structure) in detail, it is often sectioned (cut) along a surface called a plane. The section is named according to the plane in which it is cut. For example, a cut along the transverse plane produces a transverse (horizontal) section. It divides the body or organ into a superior and inferior part. A sagittal section denotes a longitudinal cut dividing the body or organ into a right and left part. A frontal (coronal section) divides the body or organ into an anterior and posterior part.

This lab exercise will provide an introduction to the use of anatomical terminology and anatomical sections. It will also introduce body cavities, abdominopelvic regions, organs and organ systems. The dissection of a rat will provide experience in the use of anatomical terminology, and an overview of the entire vertebrate body – its cavities and their contents, organs and organ systems.

Materials

1. Each pair of students should have:

    Dissection tray

    Preserved rat

    Dissection tools: scalpel, blunt probe, pointed probe, scissors, forceps, dissecting pins, twine, and disposable gloves.

2. Class materials to be shared by students:

    Models and charts of planes, cavities and organs

ACTIVITY 1:

Anatomic Terminology

Resources: Textbook: pages 11-13

Apply the following anatomic terminology to both human and animal models:

Anatomical position	Anterior	Posterior	Superior
Inferior	Cephalic (Cranial)	Caudal	Lateral
Medial	Dorsal	Ventral	Proximal
Distal	Superficial (External)	Deep (Internal)	Intermediate
Buccal	Oral	Mental	Nasal
Cervical	Thoracic	Axillary	Brachial (Arm)
Antebrachial (Forearm)	Antecubital	Otic	Occipital
Frontal	Acromial	Carpal	Palmar
Vertebral	Popliteal	Peroneal (Fibular)	Femoral (Thigh)
Lumbar	Sternal	Mammary	Scapular
Olecranal	Umbilical (Naval)	Manus	Hallux

Pollex	Inguinal	Pubic	Perineal
Patellar	Plantar	Gluteal	Coxal
Crural (Leg)	Digital	Pedal	Tarsal
Calcaneal	Sural	Orbital	Axial
Appendicular	Sacral	Abdominal	

Tips:

1. Keep in mind that the directional terms and sectional terms cannot be used interchangeably (e.g. the heart is *anterior* and not *frontal* to the spine)

2. Most of the regional terms used come from the names of muscles, bones, nerves and blood vessels.

3. When using terms like proximal and distal, keep in mind that it is in reference to the point of attachment of a limb to the trunk or the point of origin of a structure.

ACTIVITY 2:

Body Planes

Resources: Textbook: pages 14-15

Identify the following planes/sections using human and animal models and specimens:

Sagittal, Parasagittal, Midsagittal
Transverse (Horizontal)
Frontal (Coronal)

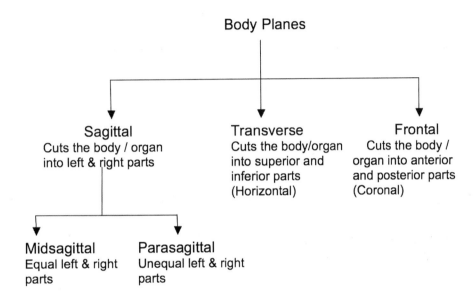

ACTIVITY 3:

Body Cavities and Abdominopelvic Regions

Resources: Textbook: pages 14-19

Identify the following cavities using human and animal models and specimens. Identify the major organs contained in the body cavities and abdominopelvic regions.

Ventral Body Cavity: Thoracic Cavity, Abominopelvic Cavity, Abdominal Cavity, and Pelvic Cavity

Dorsal Body Cavity: Cranial Cavity, Spinal (Vertebral) Cavity

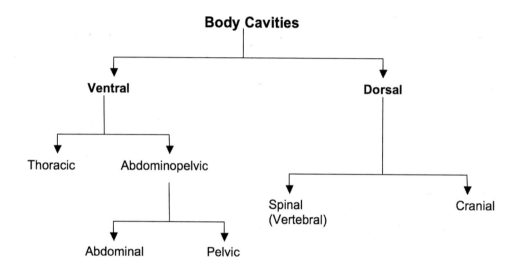

Abdominopelvic Regions:

Right Hypochondriac (hypo = below, chondro = cartilage)	Epigastric (epi = above, gastr = stomach)	Left Hypochondriac
Right Lumbar (lumbar = loins)	Umbilical	Left Lumbar
Right Iliac (inguinal)	Hypogastric	Left Iliac

ACTIVITY 4:

Organs and Organ Systems

Resources: Textbook: pages 6-7

Identify the functions and major organs involved for each of the following organ systems:

Integumentary	Cardiovascular	Reproductive
Nervous	Skeletal	Lymphatic
Muscular	Endocrine	Respiratory
Digestive	Urinary	

ACTIVITY 5:

Rat Dissection

Resources: Rat Dissection Manual: pages 16-17, 41-47 and 63-68
(Provided in lab)

Properly dissect the rat and identify the following structures:

Diaphragm	Heart	Thymus	Lungs
Trachea	Esophagus	Bronchi	Stomach
Large Intestine	Small Intestine	Cecum	Rectum
Anus	Pancreas	Spleen	Liver
Kidney	Ureter	Adrenal Gland	Urinary Bladder
Testis	Vas Deferens	Penis	Uterus
Ovary	Scrotum	Inferior Vena Cava	Superior Vena Cava
Descending Aorta	Vaginal Orifice	Mesentery	

Tips:

1. The most important precaution one has to adhere to is in the use of the scalpel. When using a scalpel, position the scalpel blade facing away from you and your partner. When making incisions, you should cut away from you. Bear in mind that this is dissection and not mutilation. Treat your rat with respect.

2. Place the animal with the ventral side up (dorsal side on the tray), and secure the limbs with pins or twine.

3. When securing the upper extremities with twine, make a loop knot around one limb, pass the twine under the tray, and then finish by making a loop knot on the other limb. Repeat for lower extremities.

4. Refer to pg. 16-17 of the Rat Dissection Manual for an incision guide for skinning.

5. **Minimal usage of scalpel is advised.** After the initial incision is made, use scissors, forceps and blunt probe to separate skin from underlying muscle. Next, hold and lift the muscle layer with the forceps, and cut through the layer, making sure that you do not go deep into the abdominal cavity and damage the organs.

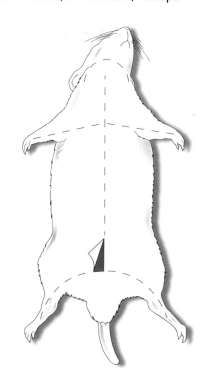

© bluedoor, LLC

6. Identify the diaphragm *before* cutting through it. Cutting the diaphragm will help loosen the rib cage.

7. Make sure you familiarize yourself with structures in both male and female rat.

8. If you would like to preserve the rat specimen for further studies please ask your lab instructor for proper method of storage.

9. When you are finished, remove all the paper towels and discard any tissues in the area designated by the instructor. Thoroughly clean and dry all the dissection tools and store them in the designated area.

Checklist:

1. _____ Anatomical position

2. _____ Anatomic terminology

3. Body planes

    _____ Sagittal, including Misagittal and Parasagittal

    _____ Transverse (Horizontal)   _____ Coronal (Frontal)

4. Body Cavities

    _____ Ventral Cavity (Thoracic, Abdominopelvic, Abdominal, Pelvic)

    _____ Dorsal Cavity (Cranial, Spinal (Vertebral))

5. Abdominopelvic Regions and their major organs

    _____ Epigastric Region   _____ Umbilical Region

    _____ R/L Hypochondriac Regions   _____ R/L Lumbar

    _____ Hypogastric (Pubic) Region   _____ R/L Iliac (Inguinal)

6. _____ Dissection of rat and identification of structures

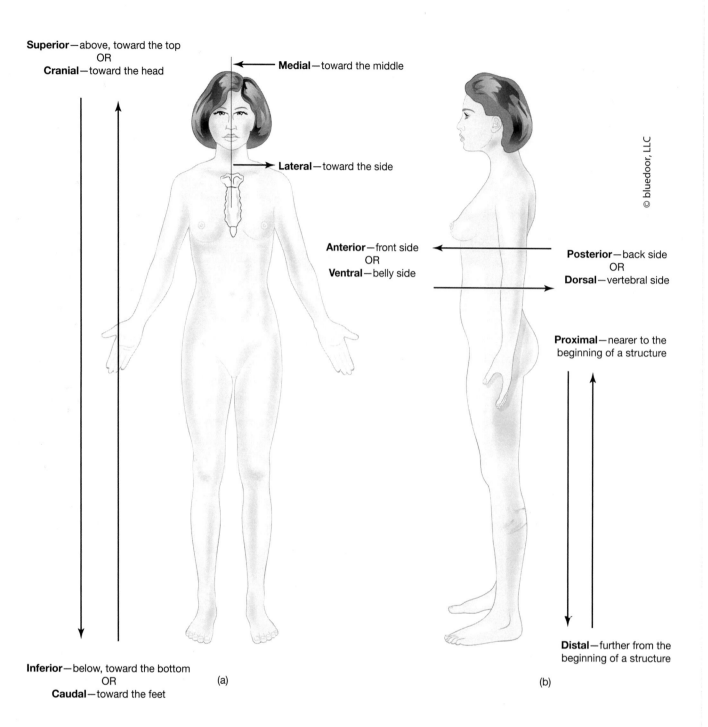

Superior—above, toward the top
OR
Cranial—toward the head

Medial—toward the middle

Lateral—toward the side

Anterior—front side
OR
Ventral—belly side

Posterior—back side
OR
Dorsal—vertebral side

Proximal—nearer to the beginning of a structure

Distal—further from the beginning of a structure

Inferior—below, toward the bottom
OR
Caudal—toward the feet

(a)

(b)

© bluedoor, LLC

Figure 1.1: Direction terms

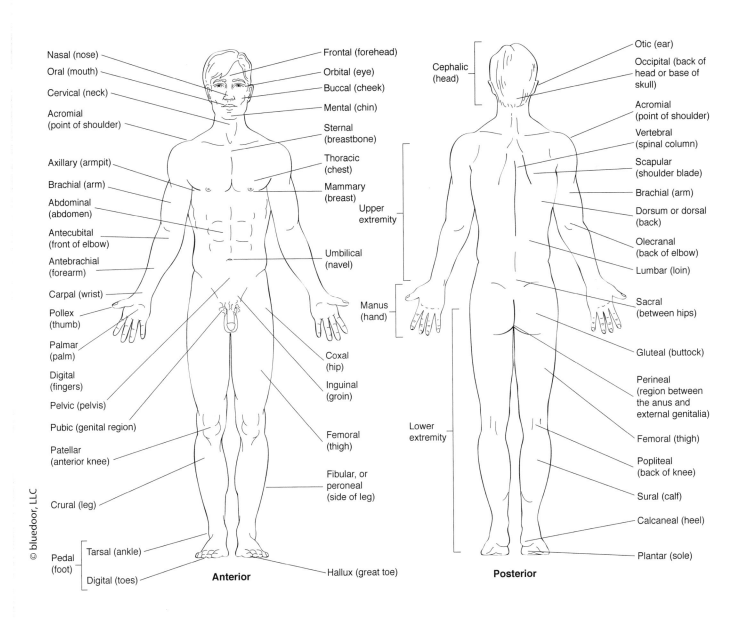

Nasal (nose)
Oral (mouth)
Cervical (neck)
Acromial (point of shoulder)
Axillary (armpit)
Brachial (arm)
Abdominal (abdomen)
Antecubital (front of elbow)
Antebrachial (forearm)
Carpal (wrist)
Pollex (thumb)
Palmar (palm)
Digital (fingers)
Pelvic (pelvis)
Pubic (genital region)
Patellar (anterior knee)
Crural (leg)
Pedal (foot)
Tarsal (ankle)
Digital (toes)

Frontal (forehead)
Orbital (eye)
Buccal (cheek)
Mental (chin)
Sternal (breastbone)
Thoracic (chest)
Mammary (breast)
Upper extremity
Umbilical (navel)
Manus (hand)
Coxal (hip)
Inguinal (groin)
Femoral (thigh)
Fibular, or peroneal (side of leg)

Anterior
Hallux (great toe)

Cephalic (head)

Otic (ear)
Occipital (back of head or base of skull)
Acromial (point of shoulder)
Vertebral (spinal column)
Scapular (shoulder blade)
Brachial (arm)
Dorsum or dorsal (back)
Olecranal (back of elbow)
Lumbar (loin)
Sacral (between hips)
Gluteal (buttock)
Perineal (region between the anus and external genitalia)
Femoral (thigh)
Popliteal (back of knee)
Sural (calf)
Calcaneal (heel)
Plantar (sole)

Lower extremity

Posterior

© bluedoor, LLC

Figure 1.2: Regional terms

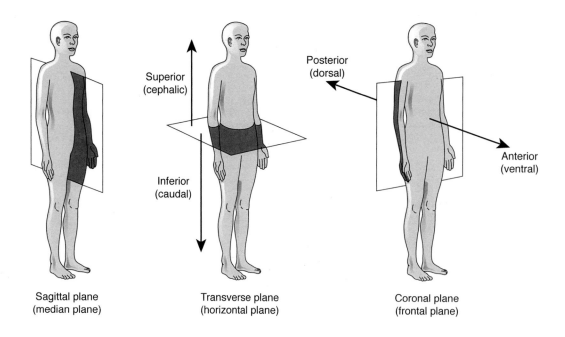

Sagittal plane
(median plane)

Superior
(cephalic)

Inferior
(caudal)

Transverse plane
(horizontal plane)

Posterior
(dorsal)

Anterior
(ventral)

Coronal plane
(frontal plane)

Figure 1.3: Planes and directional terms

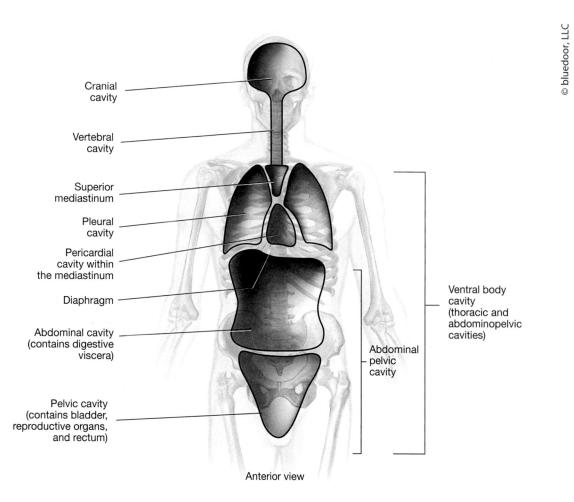

Cranial
cavity

Vertebral
cavity

Superior
mediastinum

Pleural
cavity

Pericardial
cavity within
the mediastinum

Diaphragm

Abdominal cavity
(contains digestive
viscera)

Pelvic cavity
(contains bladder,
reproductive organs,
and rectum)

Ventral body
cavity
(thoracic and
abdominopelvic
cavities)

Abdominal
pelvic
cavity

Anterior view

Figure 1.4: Body cavities, anterior view

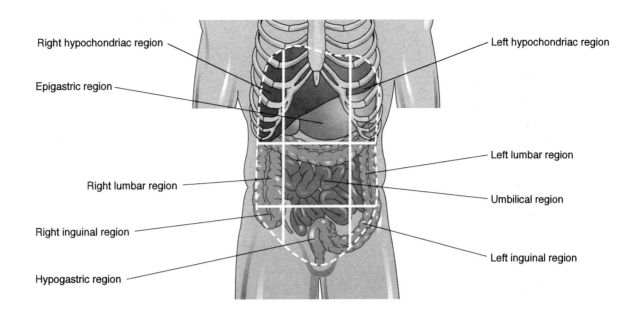

Figure 1.5: The nine abdominopelvic regions

© bluedoor, LLC

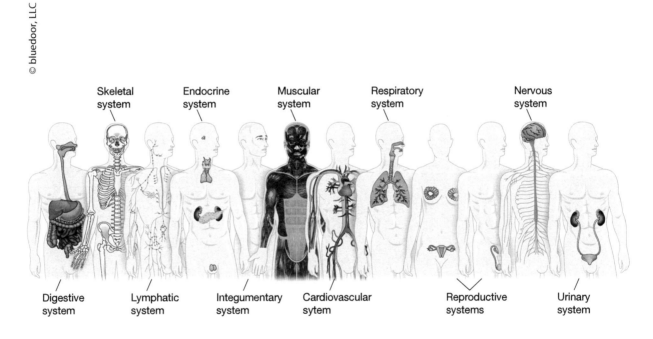

Figure 1.6: Body systems

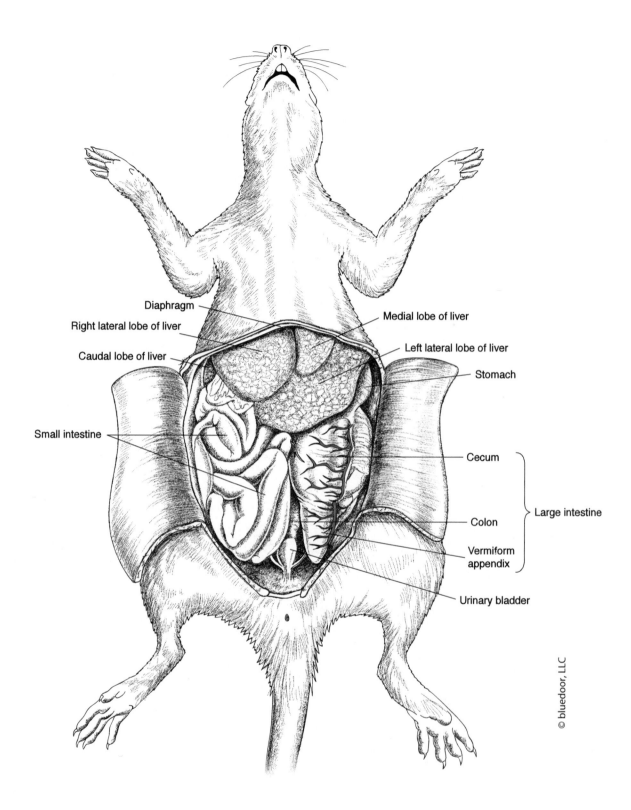

Diaphragm

Right lateral lobe of liver

Caudal lobe of liver

Medial lobe of liver

Left lateral lobe of liver

Stomach

Small intestine

Cecum

Colon

Large intestine

Vermiform appendix

Urinary bladder

© bluedoor, LLC

Figure 1.7: Abdominopelvic cavity, rat

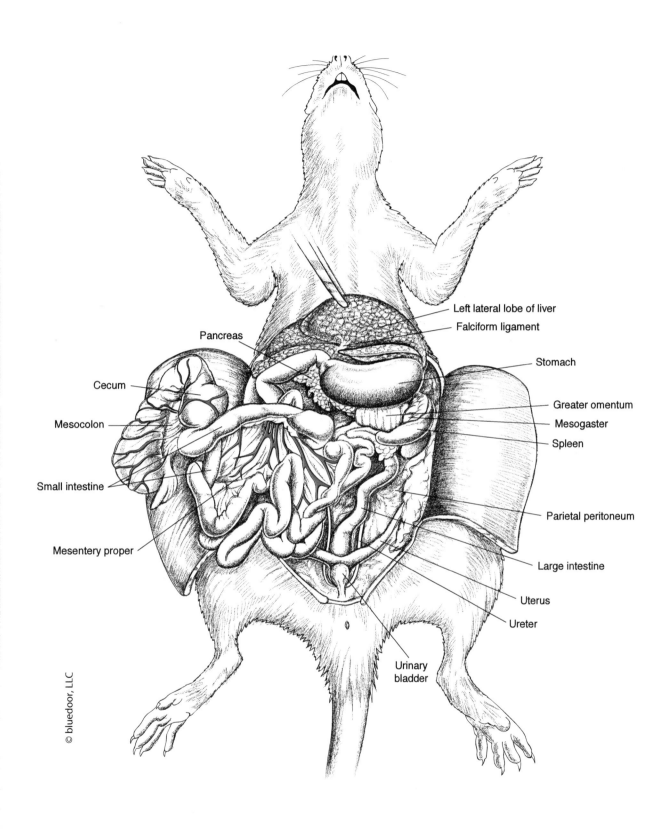

Left lateral lobe of liver

Falciform ligament

Pancreas

Stomach

Cecum

Greater omentum

Mesocolon

Mesogaster

Spleen

Small intestine

Mesentery proper

Parietal peritoneum

Large intestine

Uterus

Ureter

Urinary bladder

© bluedoor, LLC

Figure 1.8: Abdominopelvic cavity with organs displayed, female rat

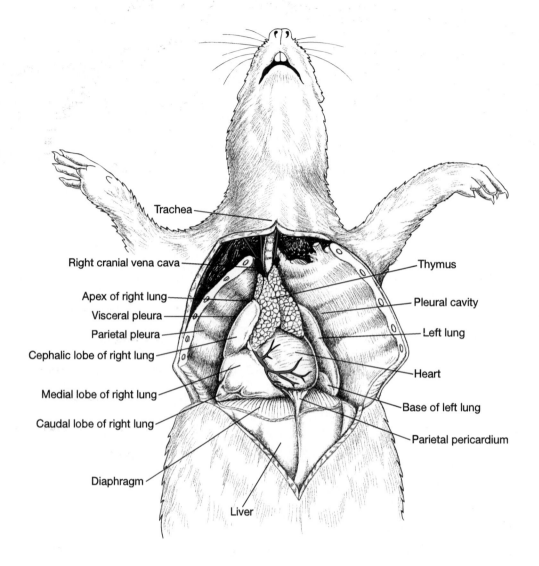

Figure 1.9: Thoracic cavity, rat

Trachea

Right cranial vena cava

Apex of right lung

Visceral pleura

Parietal pleura

Cephalic lobe of right lung

Medial lobe of right lung

Caudal lobe of right lung

Diaphragm

Liver

Thymus

Pleural cavity

Left lung

Heart

Base of left lung

Parietal pericardium

Name: _Brian Se_____ _____

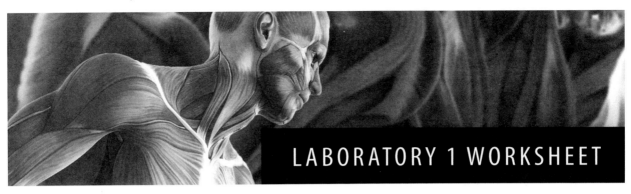

LAB 1 WORKSHEET

1. Describe the standard anatomical position. _____

   _____

   _____

2. Define "section". _____

   _____

   _____

3. Anatomic terminology. Please provide the correct anatomical term or the common term as specified.

   a. Sometimes injections are given in the buttocks. The correct anatomical term for this region is the _gluteal_____ region.

   b. While bicycling, an 8 year old boy fell down and skinned his **forehead**. The area referred to here is the ~~cranial~~ frontal_ area.

   c. The doctor told the patient that the probable reason for the pain in the **inguinal** region could be a hernia. Which area is she referring to? ___groin_____frontal_____

   d. Mr. S was told that he had a huge mass in his **armpit** and had to have surgery done. This region is the _axillary_____.

   e. Your friend had surgery to relieve **carpal** tunnel syndrome. The surgery was performed on his wrist_____.

   f. The respiratory diaphragm is _inferior_____ to the lungs and _superior_____ to the liver.

   g. The lungs are _lateral_____ to the heart.

   h. The trachea is _superior_____ to the esophagus.

   i. The elbow is _distal____ **(proximal/distal)** to the wrist.

j. The ankle is _dostal_ **(proximal/distal)** to the knee.

k. The patella is on the _so_ surface of the lower limb.

l. The skin is _superficial_ to the muscles of your body.

4. Indicate the following body areas on the accompanying diagram by placing the correct word at the end of each line.

a. sural   b. pollex   c. popliteal   d. sternal   e. manus   f. vertebral   g. crural

h. otic   i. cervical   j. brachial   k. gluteal   l. tarsal   m. antebrachial   n. plantar

Otic
Cervical
Sternal
brachial
antebrachial
manus
crural
tarsal

Vertebral
gluteal
pollex
popliteal
sural
plantar

5. Complete each statement below by choosing the appropriate term from the key.

midsagittal   frontal   transverse   parasagittal   sagittal

a. If an incision cuts the brain into superior and inferior portions, that section is called _transverse_. If the incision cuts the brain into equal right and left parts, this section is a _midsagittal_ section.

b. In what type of section is it possible to observe both dorsal and ventral body cavities in the same section? _frontal_ and _transverse_

c. Two planes of section can be used to show portions of both right and left lungs in the same section. Which two sections are these? _sagittal_ and _frontal_

6. Correctly identify each of the nine areas of the abdominopelvic surface and write the appropriate term on the corresponding line.

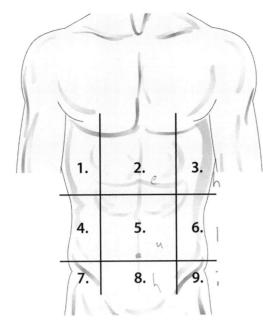

1. right hypochondriac
2. epigastric
3. left hypochondriac
4. right lumbar
5. umbilical
6. left lumbar
7. right inguinal
8. hypogastric
9. left inguinal

7. Using the key below, place the following organs or structures in their proper body cavity

a. thoracic   b. spinal   c. cranial   d. abdominal   e. pelvic

_b_ spinal cord   _e_ rectum   _e_ uterus

_a_ aorta   _b_ trachea   _a_ pituitary gland

_d_ pancreas   _e_ lungs   _e_ gall bladder

8. Use the list below to indicate the body systems that perform the following functions.

cardiovascular   urinary   integumentary   nervous   skeletal
reproductive   digestive   muscular   endocrine   respiratory
lymphatics/immunity

Controls the body by means of hormones   _endocrine_

Breaks down food, absorbs nutrients   _digestive_

Control and coordination of other
systems, processing information   _nervous_

Removal of carbon dioxide from the blood   _respiratory_

Supports the body, aids in movement   _skeletal_

Eliminates nitrogen containing waste,
maintains acid-base balance   _urinary_

Protects the body, destroys bacteria
and tumor cells   _lymphatic_

Produces movement, maintains posture
and produces body heat   _muscular_

Aids in conception and childbearing   _reproductive_

Includes the heart and major blood vessels   _cardiovascular_

Delivers oxygen and nutrients to the body   _respiratory_ CARDIO.

Protects underlying organs from drying out,
and from mechanical damage   _integumentary_

Causes onset of the menstrual cycle   _endocrine_

9.   Choose the organ system to which the following structures belong:

mammary glands, ovary, uterus   ~~endocrine~~ reproductive

thyroid gland, pituitary, testes   _reproductive_

scrotum, prostate gland, seminal vesicle _reproductive_

hair, nails, sweat glands   _integumentary_

liver, pancreas, stomach   _digestive_

trachea, bronchi, alveoli   _respiratory_

spleen, thymus, lymph nodes   _endocrine_

vertebrae, hip joint, femur   _skeletal_

nerves, brain, spinal cord   ~~~~ _nervous_

urethra, bladder, ureters   _urinary_

10. Place the following organs in the appropriate abdominopelvic region:

stomach   _abdominal_

gall bladder   _pelvic_

urinary bladder   _pelvic_

pancreas   _abdominal_

uterus   _pelvic_

spleen   _abdominal_

11. The _diaphragm_ divides the thoracic from the abdominopelvic cavity.

12. What abdominal organ does the human have that the rat is missing? _____

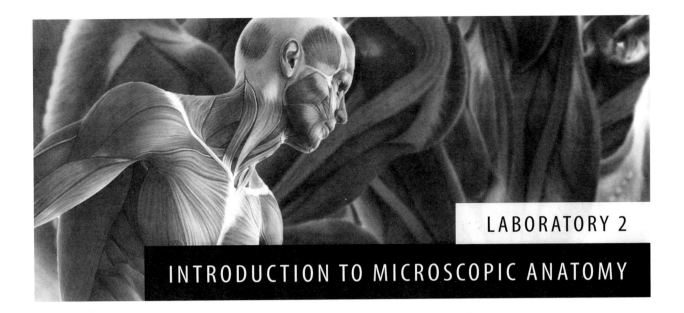

INTRODUCTION TO MICROSCOPIC ANATOMY

Objectives:

1. Identify the major components of a binocular compound microscope and identify their functions.

2. Properly use a microscope to focus on specimens using each of the objective lenses.

3. Define the following terms: total magnification, resolution, microscopic field, working distance, parfocal and contrast.

4. Differentiate between the following specimen preparation methods used to prepare tissues for microscopy: whole mount, smear, squash, cross section, longitudinal section.

5. Describe the three major parts of a typical mammalian cell.

6. Identify the ectoderm, endoderm, and mesoderm of a late gastrula and identify the tissues to which they give rise in the fully-developed organism.

INTRODUCTION

The microscope is a biologist's most powerful observational tool. A light microscope functions by enlarging the image of an object illuminated by sunlight or an electric light source. Enlargement of the image is achieved when glass lenses bend the light rays that pass through the image. The rays that carry the image are focused at a position on the opposite slide of the lens, generating beyond this focal point an enlarged inverted image of the object. Microscopes used in modern biology labs are compound microscopes, and the light passes through two lenses arranged in series. This provides greater magnification than the use of a single lens.

The quality of a microscopic image is determined by magnification, resolution and contrast. Proper adjustment of the microscope will maximize these qualities and help to reduce eye strain.

This lab exercise will focus on proper use of the binocular compound light microscope and its application to the study of human cells. The diversity of cell structure and the specialization of cell function will be stressed.

Review the information below before you begin.

I. **Care and Storage: Every part of a good quality microscope is incredibly expensive, so be very careful when handling it.**

    1. Use two hands to carry the microscope. Place one hand under the base and use the other to hold the arm. Always keep the microscope in an upright position.

    2. Always place the microscope on a flat surface and make sure that it is not too close to the edge of the lab bench.

    3. Clean every lens before and after use. Use lens paper only, and if necessary, lens cleaner. Never use any other materials to clean the lenses.

    4. Always turn off the light when not actually using the microscope.

    5. Always unplug the electrical cord by pulling on the plug, not the cord.

    6. Never remove parts from the microscope. Notify the lab instructor if there is a problem – don't try to fix it yourself.

    7. When you are finished with the microscope, return it to its numbered location in the microscope cabinet.

    8. Microscopes should be stored with the lowest-powered objective lens in position and the lens should be positioned as close to the stage as possible (use the coarse adjustment knob). Remember to remove any slides from the stage and return it to its proper location.

    9. Focus smoothly; don't try to speed through the focusing process.

    10. Always begin focusing using either the scanning or the low power

    11. (10X) objective. Because the microscopes are parfocal, an image brought into focus at low power will be quickly and easily focused at high power.

    12. Only use oil when using the 100X (oil immersion) lens; always use oil when using the 100X lens. Always clean the slide and the oil immersion lens after use using the lens cleaner solution and lens paper.

II. Parts of the Microscope

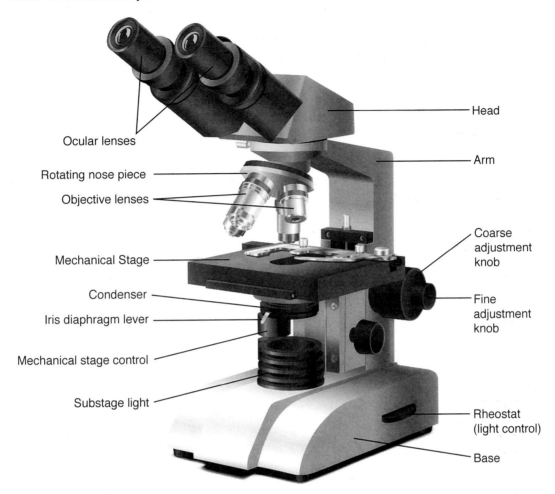

Ocular lenses

Rotating nose piece

Objective lenses

Mechanical Stage

Condenser

Iris diaphragm lever

Mechanical stage control

Substage light

Head

Arm

Coarse adjustment knob

Fine adjustment knob

Rheostat (light control)

Base

© bluedoor, LLC

Ocular lens:	also called an eyepiece. The microscopes in our lab have two eyepieces at the superior end of the body tube (binocular). The ocular lenses on your microscope have a magnification power of 10X. One of the ocular lenses has a pointer in it that may be positioned by rotating that ocular lens.
Body tube:	Holds the ocular lenses in place.
Revolving nosepiece:	A circular mechanism located at the bottom of the body tube and attached to three or four objective lenses. It can be rotated to position the desired lens in the light path.
Objective lens:	One of either three or four magnifying lenses attached to the revolving nosepiece. Each objective lens is marked with its magnification factor and is marked with unique colored rings for quick identification. Microscopes may have any or all of the following objective lenses:
scanning lens:	either 4X or 5X; use this for initial location of a specimen
10X (low power) lens:	may also be used to locate a specimen; this objective lens may be suitable for viewing some specimens that do not need greater magnification

40X (high power) lens:	also called a high, dry objective; used for specimens that require a greater degree of magnification
100X (oil immersion) lens:	used for viewing extremely small objects, such as blood cells or bacterial cells; this lens must be immersed in oil when in use
Note:	Lower-powered lenses are short in length and higher powered lenses are longer.
Mechanical stage:	Flat, horizontal platform below the objective lenses that the slide rests on. The stage has an opening so the light can pass through the specimen from below. This stage is equipped with a mechanical device that can be used to move the slide backwards and forward and side to side.
Substage light:	A high-intensity light source. Light rays from this source pass through the specimen, through the objective lens and the ocular lenses to the eye.
Condenser:	A small lens located beneath the stage that concentrates the light onto the specimen. The condenser can be raised and lowered. For most work, the condenser should be positioned as close to the stage as possible (raised position).
Iris diaphragm:	Regulates the amount of light that passes through the specimen. The diaphragm is adjusted by rotating a lever attached to the side of the device.
Coarse adjustment knob:	Used to bring the specimen into focus by increasing or decreasing the distance between the objective lens and the specimen.
Fine Adjustment knob:	Like for coarse adjustment knob, but is used for finer focusing after coarse focusing knob has been used.

III. Focusing Procedure

1. Turn on the light source.

2. Secure the slide in place on the stage using the brackets. Use the mechanical stage device to position the specimen as best as you can over the light beam passing through the slide. (Note: make sure that the slide is clean and avoid getting fingerprints on the cover slip).

3. Place the lowest powered objective (4X or 10X) into position using the revolving nosepiece. Bring the objective and stage as close together as possible using the coarse adjustment knob.

4. Look through the ocular lens and adjust the light intensity using the iris diaphragm. With a binocular microscope you need to adjust the eyepiece separation just like you do a pair of binoculars. Make sure that the substage condenser is in its highest position.

5. Use the coarse adjustment knob to slowly move the slide and the objective lens apart. When the image becomes clear, switch to the fine adjustment to make the image sharper.

6. One or both of the eyepieces may be a telescoping eyepiece that is, you can focus it. Since very few people have eyes that are perfectly matched, most of us need to focus one eyepiece to match the other image. Look with the appropriate eye into the fixed eyepiece and focus with the microscope focus knob. Next, look into the adjustable eyepiece (with the other eye of course), and adjust the eyepiece, not the microscope.

7. If you wish to view the specimen using a higher magnification (either 10X or 40X), rotate the next higher magnification lens into position without touching either the coarse or fine adjustment knobs. These microscopes are parfocal, that is, once a specimen is in focus at low magnification, it remains focused when higher objectives are placed into position.

8. Some minor adjustment with the fine adjustment knob may be needed. Never adjust the focus using the coarse adjustment knob when using the 40X or 100X lens. Readjust the diaphragm to increase the light intensity if necessary.

9. You may wish to use the 100X (oil immersion) lens for very small objects. If so, first focus on the object using the 40X lens, as described above. Then, follow these steps:

   a. Center the object that you are interested in magnifying in the center of the field.

   b. Using the revolving nosepiece, swing the 40X objective lens out of the way, about halfway to the next position.

   c. Carefully place a small drop of immersion oil directly on the slide over the center of the region of interest.

   d. Rotate the oil immersion objective into position

   e. Using the fine focus and looking through the ocular lens, focus on the specimen. It will probably be necessary to increase the light intensity using the iris diaphragm.

   f. Make sure that you clean the lens and the slide when you are finished.

Note: Never use an oil immersion lens without the oil. Never get oil on any other lens. Clean up all oil when finished.

IV. Useful Terms

Contrast: The difference in intensity between the specimen and the surrounding background. It is most conveniently altered by using the iris diaphragm located below the substage condenser.

Field of vision: the surface area which can be seen when looking through the light microscope. The area decreases with increasing power of magnification.

Resolution: The ability to distinguish between closely positioned objects. The human eye can resolve objects that are about 100 μm apart. Under ideal conditions, the compound light microscope has a resolving power of 0.2 μm. Without good resolution, magnified objects may appear blurry and indistinct. Resolution is specified as "r", the minimum distance at which the objects can be perceived as distinct from each other. Thus, the smaller the "r", the better the resolution

Total magnification: The perceived increase in the size of an object when viewed using a microscope. TM is equal to the magnifying power of the ocular lens multiplied by the magnifying power of the objective lens being used; thus for a 10X ocular lens and a high dry objective, the total magnification is 10X x 40X, or 400X.

Working distance: The distance between the bottom of the objective lens and the top of the cover glass on the slide. The higher the magnification the smaller the working distance. The working distance between the highest powered objective and the slide can be less than a mm, so care must be taken to keep an objective lens from hitting the slide.

MATERIALS

1. Each student should have a compound microscope.

2. Each pair of students should have:

Lens Paper

Immersion Oil

Lens Cleaner

Box of prepared slides

Colored pencils

ACTIVITY 1:

Using A Compound Microscope

1. Use a prepared slide of the letter "e" for this section.

   a. Remove a prepared slide of the "letter e" from the box and look at the letter under the cover slip with your unassisted eye (the slide label should be on the left). Sketch the letter e in the space found in Question #1 of the Lab Activities Worksheet.

   b. Secure the slide on the stage of your microscope and bring the letter e into focus using the lowest-powered objective (follow the directions below). Sketch the letter e as it appears in the field in the space found in Question #1 of the Lab Activities Worksheet.

   c. Move the slide slowly away from you on the stage using the mechanical stage while continuing to view it through the ocular lenses. Note the direction the image moves in Question #1 of the Lab Activities Worksheet.

   d. Move the slide slowly to the right using the mechanical stage while continuing to view it through the ocular lenses. Note the direction the image moves in Question #1 of the Lab Activities Worksheet.

e. Increase the magnification using the low-powered objective and refocus. Use the iris diaphragm to increase the amount of light passing though the specimen. When you are satisfied with the image, increase the magnification to the high dry objective and refocus. Answer the remaining portions of Question #1 of the Lab Activities Worksheet.

ACTIVITY 2:

Slide Preparation: Sectioning and Mounting Specimens

Resources: Textbook: page 1032

Review the material below before you begin this activity:

1. Go to the demonstration area and view the slides that demonstrate various types of slide preparations:

> Lymph: wm
> Renal (kidney) tubule: ls
> Renal (kidney) tubule: cs (ts)
> Sperm: sm
> Chromosomes: sq

2. Make drawings of each slide in Question #2 of the Lab Activities Sheet.

Background Information

Even if you know what type of specimen you would like to examine, there are a variety of ways to prepare the specimen for the finished microscope slide. Here are some of the preparations used for human cells and tissues:

Whole mount: An entire structure, uncut, is embedded in mounting resin directly on the slide and covered with a glass coverslip.

Smear or Drop: The specimen(s) are in suspension then dried directly onto the glass slide where they are fixed, stained, and mounted in resin under a coverslip. This preparation is usually used for blood cells or semen.

Squash: The cell specimen is broken using pressure – usually used to release chromosomes from nuclei, then processed as a smear is.

Section: A thin piece of specimen is shaved from the whole specimen to permit light to reveal greater structural detail. Sections are usually between 10 and 100 microns thick, which is usually thicker than one cell diameter. Therefore, several layers of cells may be present in the section. Some sections, called thin sections, are on the order of 1 micron thick, which is usually less than one cell diameter. Therefore, subcellular structures are more easily discerned than in thicker sections.

Sections can be either longitudinal sections which are made lengthwise, parallel to the long axis of the structure, or transverse (cross sections) which are made perpendicular to the long axis.

Look at the label of a prepared slide to determine how the specimen has been prepared. "Wm" means whole mount (the complete structure); "cs" is a cross section, such as a thin transverse section; "ls" is a longitudinal section, a section cut lengthwise; "sq" is a squash preparation; and, "sm" is a smear, such as a blood smear.

ACTIVITY 3:

Generalized mammalian cell

Read the material below before you begin this activity:

The basic structural unit of the body is the cell. Cells must maintain boundaries, take in nutrients, dispose of wastes, reproduce, grow, move, and undergo metabolism. While cells of the human body are varied in their morphology they all have three major parts: the plasma membrane, cytoplasm, and nucleus.

Resources: Textbook: Pages 62-63, page 120 (Fig. 4.3)

1. Focus on a single cell on the microscope slide. Draw one cell from the specimen and label the plasma membrane, cytoplasm, and nucleus.

ACTIVITY 4:

Embryonic Germ Layers

Read the material below before you begin this exercise.

1. Use the models and/or prepared slide in the lab to identify the primary germ layers of a gastrula.

2. Make a labeled drawing in Question #4 of the Lab Worksheet.

A stem cell is a cell that has the ability to self-replicate (divide) for indefinite periods, perhaps throughout the entire life of an organism. In addition to replicating, stem cells may also differentiate into any of the mature cells that make up each of the tissues of the organism. These mature cells have characteristics sizes, shapes and composition, along with specialized functions.

A fertilized egg is often referred to as a **totipotent stem cell**, since it has the capacity to divide and produce cells that may differentiate into any of the cells of the mature organism. After an egg is fertilized it begins a series of rapid mitotic divisions, forming a ball of cells (day 3) called a morula. The cells of the morula continue to divide, and reorganization of the structure occurs, leading to the formation of a blastocyst (day 4) and then a layered structure called a gastrula (day 16). The cells of the embryonic germ layers of the gastrula are called **pluripotent stem cells** because they can each give rise to a more limited variety of cell types. The differentiation of stem cells is regulated by intrinsic signals and by the external microenvironment.

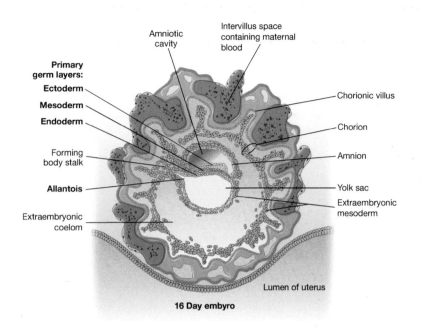

© bluedoor, LLC

16 Day embyro

Ectoderm: brain, spinal cord, all other neurons, sensory receptors, adrenal medulla, skin (epidermis), pituitary gland, connective tissue of head

Mesoderm: muscles, blood, bone, sex organs, adrenal cortex, lymphatic tissue, urogenital system, heart and blood vessels, most connective tissues

Endoderm: lining of gut, lining of lungs, lining of the bladder, liver, pancreas, larynx, trachea, lung, thymus gland, thyroid, parathyroid gland, urinary bladder, vagina, urethra

Checklist:

A. Microscopy

Location and functions of:

____Ocular lens

____Body tube

____Revolving nosepiece

____Mechanical stage

____Substage light

____Condenser

____Iris diaphragm

____Coarse adjustment knob

____Fine adjustment knob

Terminology

____Contrast

____Field of vision

____Resolution

____Total magnification

____Working distance

B. Preparing specimens

_____Types of preparations (wm, sm, sq, etc.)

C. Cells

_____Simple squamous cell

D. Embryonic germ layers

_____Ectoderm   _____Mesoderm   _____Endoderm

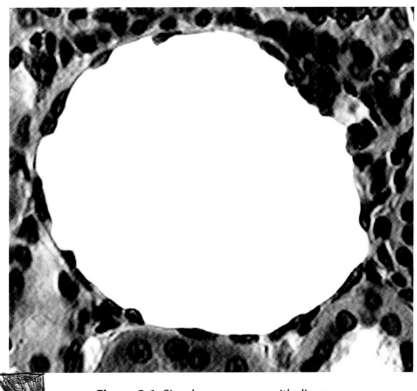

Figure 2.1: Simple squamous epithelium

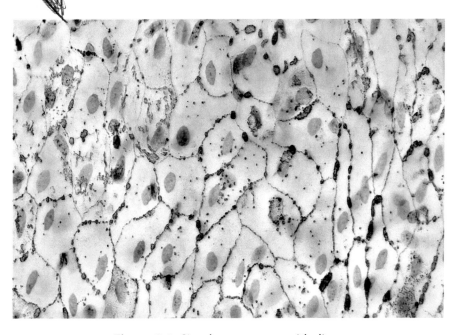

Figure 2.2: Simple squamous epithelium

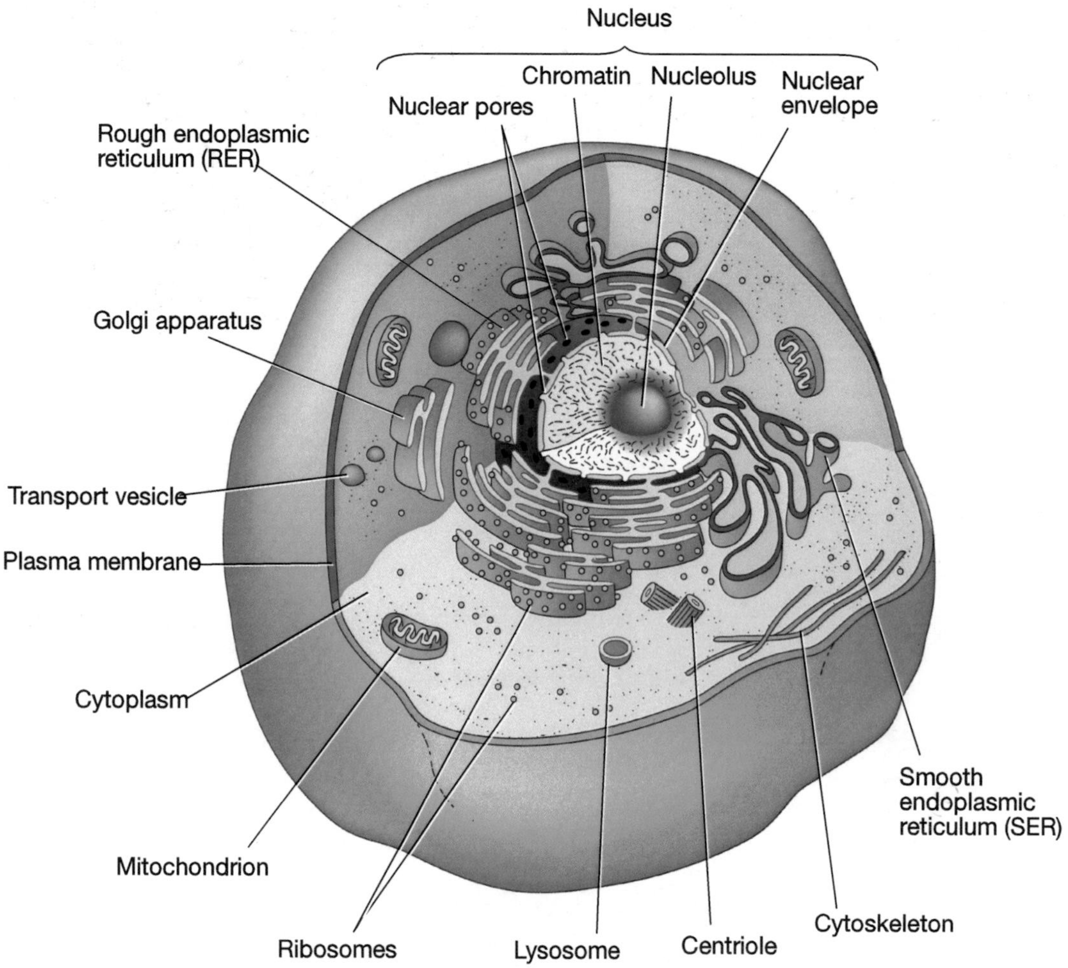

Figure 2.3: Typical animal cell.

Name: _____ JC

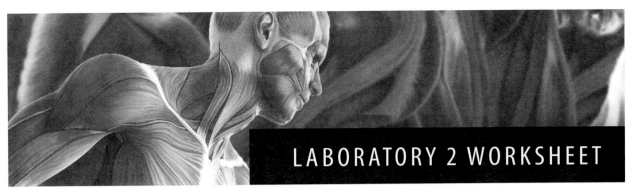

LAB 2 WORKSHEET

1. Microscopic Techniques:

   a. Draw the letter "e" as it appears under each magnification and note the total magnification (TM) for each image:

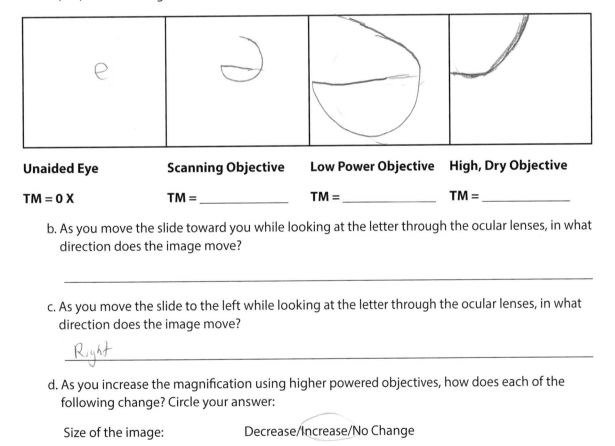

Unaided Eye	Scanning Objective	Low Power Objective	High, Dry Objective
TM = 0 X	TM = _____	TM = _____	TM = _____

   b. As you move the slide toward you while looking at the letter through the ocular lenses, in what direction does the image move?

   _____

   c. As you move the slide to the left while looking at the letter through the ocular lenses, in what direction does the image move?

   _Right_____

   d. As you increase the magnification using higher powered objectives, how does each of the following change? Circle your answer:

   Size of the image: Decrease/Increase/No Change

   Size the field: Decrease/Increase/No Change

   Working distance: Decrease/Increase/No Change

e. Is it better to increase or decrease the light intensity as you change to a higher magnification?

decrease

2. Specimen Preparation

Make sketches of the specimens at the demonstration area:

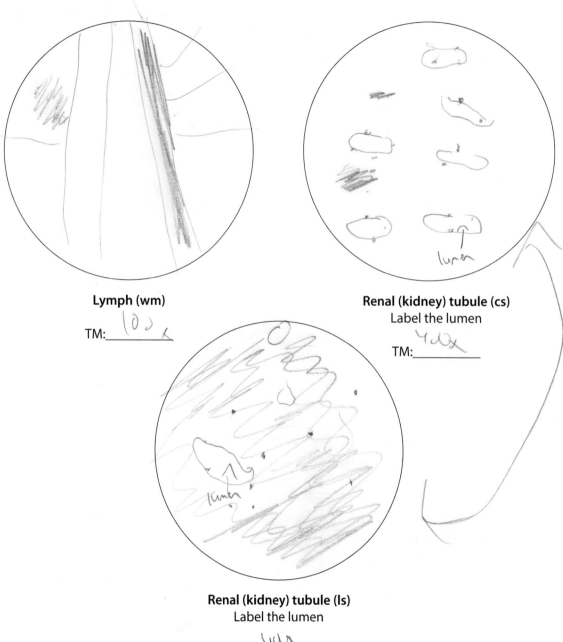

Lymph (wm)

TM:_100x_

Renal (kidney) tubule (cs)
Label the lumen

TM:_40x_

Renal (kidney) tubule (ls)
Label the lumen

TM:_40x_

3. Generalized cell

Prepare a labeled sketch of the following slide as seen under the microscope:

Sperm (sm)

TM:_____100x_____

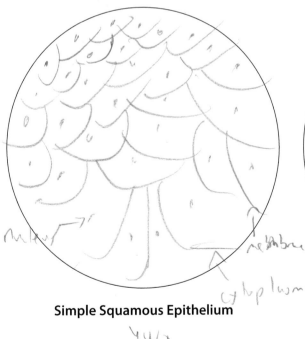

Chromosomes (sq)

TM:_____1000x_____

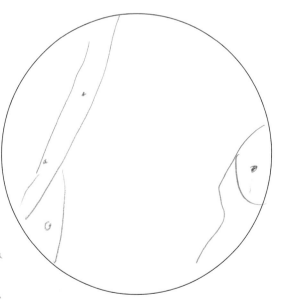

Simple Squamous Epithelium

TM:_____4wx_____

Label: nucleus, cytoplasm, and plasma membrane

Simple Squamous Epithelium (cs)

TM:_____100x_____

4. Development

a. Make a sketch of a gastrula and label the endoderm, ectoderm and mesoderm.

Gastrula

Total magnification: (100k

Label: ectoderm, mesoderm, and endoderm

b. Indicate from which embryonic layer the following tissues/organs develop:

Thyroid gland

~~ectoderm~~ endoderm

Cardiac muscle

mesoderm

Cartilage

~~endoderm~~ ectoderm

POST LAB WORKSHEET LAB 2

1. Complete, or respond to, the following questions:

a. The _____ is a lens under the stage that concentrates the light.

Condenser

b. The area of a slide seen when looking through a microscope is the:

field of view

c. If the stage has a device that moves the slide from side to side and up or down, the stage is called a(n) _____ stage.

mechanical

d. The ability to distinguish between closely positioned objects is called:

resolution

e. If, after focusing using a low power objective lens only the fine adjustment needs to be used to focus under a higher power, the microscope is said to be:

f. If a microscope has a 10X ocular lens and the objective lens in use is the 100X, what is the total magnification achieved?

1000x

g. The distance from the bottom of the objective lens to the specimen is called the:

h. The set of lenses closest to the viewer's eyes are:

i. What device allows the user to alter the amount of light that passes through a specimen from a light source?

j. You are looking into the microscope and are surprised to see that only half of the field is illuminated. What is the probable cause?

k. You are viewing a specimen using a microscope and you attempt to change the position of the specimen in the field using the mechanical stage. You are surprised when the slide does not move. What is the probable cause?

l. The letter "J" appears in this orientation under the cover slip of a microscope slide. How will this letter appear when viewed using a microscope? (Draw it in the space):

2. Indicate which type of preparation (whole mount, smear, longitudinal section, cross section or squash) you would use in the following situations:

To do a blood cell count

To view the lumen (opening) in the trachea

To view an entire, intact human embryo _____

To view the internal tissues of a tooth
 from the superior portion to the inferior portion _____

To release pathogens from infected
cells in preparation for microscopy _____

3. Using your textbook, determine the function(s) of the following:

Plasma Membrane: _____

Cytoplasm: _____

Nucleus: _____

4. Indicate whether the tissue/cell below is derived from ectoderm (EC), mesoderm (ME), or endoderm (EN):

_____ liver   _____ skin (epidermis)

_____ lymphatic tissue   _____ heart

_____ brain and spinal cord   _____ adrenal medulla

_____ bones   _____ blood

_____ lining of the respiratory tract   _____ thyroid gland

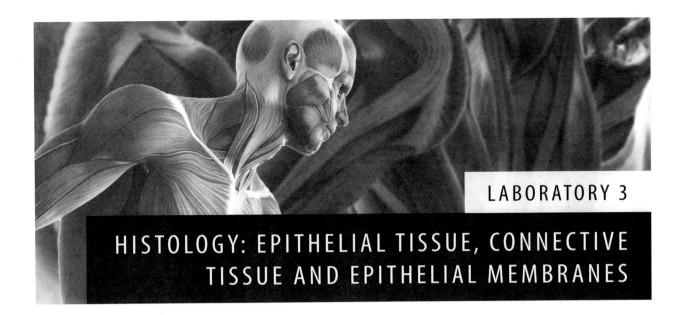

HISTOLOGY: EPITHELIAL TISSUE, CONNECTIVE TISSUE AND EPITHELIAL MEMBRANES

Objectives

1. Identify the following epithelial tissues using a prepared slide or diagram: simple squamous, simple cuboidal, simple columnar, pseudostratified columnar, stratified squamous, stratified cuboidal, stratified columnar, and transitional. Indicate the function and location(s) of the tissue.

2. Identify the following connective tissues using a prepared slide or a diagram: Connective tissues: embryonic (mesenchyme), areolar, adipose, reticular, dense regular, dense irregular, hyaline cartilage, elastic cartilage and fibrocartilage. Indicate the function and location(s) of the tissue.

3. Given a prepared slide of a mucous membrane, identify it as belonging to the trachea or esophagus. Be able to identify the different epithelium that may be associated with a mucous membrane.

INTRODUCTION

A tissue is composed of groups of cells that are similar in structure, and function together to carry out one or more common or related activities. Body tissues are classified into four basic categories: epithelial tissue, connective tissue, muscle tissue and nervous tissue. The tissues of the body are vastly different with respect to the types of cells present, the arrangement of cells and the amount and type of extracellular material.

Epithelial membranes are simple organs that are composed of a superficial layer of epithelial tissue and an underlying layer of vascular connective tissue.

The primary epithelial membranes of the body are mucous membranes, serous membranes and the cutaneous membrane (skin).

The microscopic study of tissue is called histology. This laboratory exercise will provide an introduction to the microscopic study of epithelial tissues, connective tissues and two epithelial membranes (mucous membranes and serous membranes). This will ensure a better understanding of organ structure and function when the body systems are studied in the future. Muscle tissue and nervous tissue will be the focus of future lab exercises.

Materials

1. Each student should have a compound microscope.

2. Each pair of students should have:

    Lens Paper   Colored Pencils

    Immersion Oil   Box of Prepared Slides

    Lens Cleaner

ACTIVITY 1:

Examination of Epithelial Tissues

Resources: Textbook: pages 118-124

Examine prepared slides of the following epithelial tissues under the microscope and prepare labeled sketches of each one:

Simple Squamous   Stratified Squamous

Simple Cuboidal   Transitional

Simple Columnar   Pseudostratified columnar

Tips:

1. Before you begin to search for a particular tissue on a prepared slide, review the photomicrographs in the textbook and in the following pages.

2. Frequently, the prepared slide is a section of an organ that includes multiple types of tissue, including the one that you are interested in studying. It is a good idea to scan the specimen under low power to locate the tissue that you want to examine. For epithelial tissues, you should look at the edge of the specimen, or the lining of tubes, because epithelial tissue often lines spaces. Once the tissue has been identified, move to progressively higher power until you see the tissue in sufficient detail.

3. For most specimens, the cell cytoplasm will appear pale pink or gray and the nucleus will appear dark blue or violet. The plasma membrane may be distinct or indistinct.

4. Note the shape of the nucleus. Squamous cells will have a disc-shaped nucleus, cuboidal cells will have a rounded nucleus and for columnar cells, the nucleus is oval-shaped.

5. For simple epithelium, observe the cell shape and try to locate a basement membrane and other details, such as any goblet cells, microvilli or cilia that might be present. Microvilli and cilia can be seen best using the 100X (oil immersion) objective. For stratified epithelium, observe the shape

of the apical cells, the shape of the basal cells, and the number of cell layers. Try to locate the basement membrane as well. You might want to draw the apical cells and the basal cells using different colors.

6. Keep in mind that the cell shape that you visualize is related to the type of section that was made. For example, viewed from the side, simple squamous epithelium looks like a line of thin cells. If, on the other hand, it is viewed as a sheet from above, the tissue looks like a sheet of polygonal cells, much like a tile floor.

7. If you are having trouble distinguishing between two tissue types (say, transitional vs. stratified squamous), consider comparing them on two different microscopes placed alongside each other. Look at each one, going back and forth between the two microscopes, until you feel comfortable differentiating them. Try to determine the unique characteristics that make these tissues different.

8. Use this key to help you determine an epithelial tissue classification:

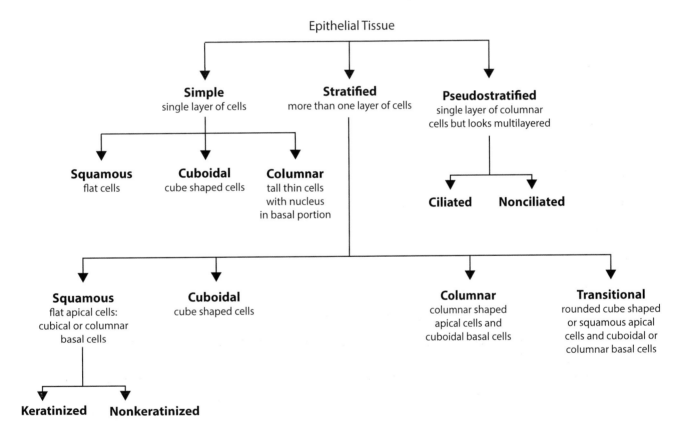

ACTIVITY 2:

Examination of Connective Tissues

Resources: Textbook: pages 127-136

Examine prepared slides of the following connective tissues under the microscope and prepare labeled sketches of each one:

embryonic (mesenchyme)	areolar	adipose
reticular	dense regular	dense irregular
hyaline cartilage	elastic cartilage	fibrocartilage

Tips:

Most of the previous tips still apply, but here a few more:

1. In most cases there is a great deal of nonliving extracellular matrix between the cells of the tissue. The matrix consists of ground substance (interstitial fluid, cell adhesion proteins and proteoglycans) and fibers (collagen, elastic and/or reticular).

2. Stained elastic fibers often appear as dark, thin jagged strands. Stained collagen fibers often appear as thicker hazy pink or light purple, sometimes crisscrossing lines. Reticular fibers are not usually visible unless they are stained with special dyes. If they are visible they may appear as delicate green or black fibers that branch to form a three-dimensional network.

3. The chondrocytes of cartilage are located in spaces called lacunae. In stained preparations the chondrocytes are usually pink to violet and appear to have shriveled within their respective lacunae. The collagen fibers of hyaline cartilage are not distinct in the smooth, pinkish or lavender matrix. Elastic fibers are obvious in the matrix of elastic cartilage and collagen fibers are obvious in the matrix of fibrocartilage.

4. Adipose tissue lacks some of the typical connective tissue described above. The adipocytes (cells) store fat in vesicles that are so large the cytoplasm and organelles are pushed into a thin ring just under the plasma membrane. As the cells fill up with fat and enlarge, they crowd the fibers and other cells. Therefore, adipose tissue has little extracellular material compared to other types of connective tissue.

5. Use this key to help you to determine a connective tissue classification (note: there are connective tissues such as blood and bone that are not included in this flow chart; they will be examined in other lab sessions):

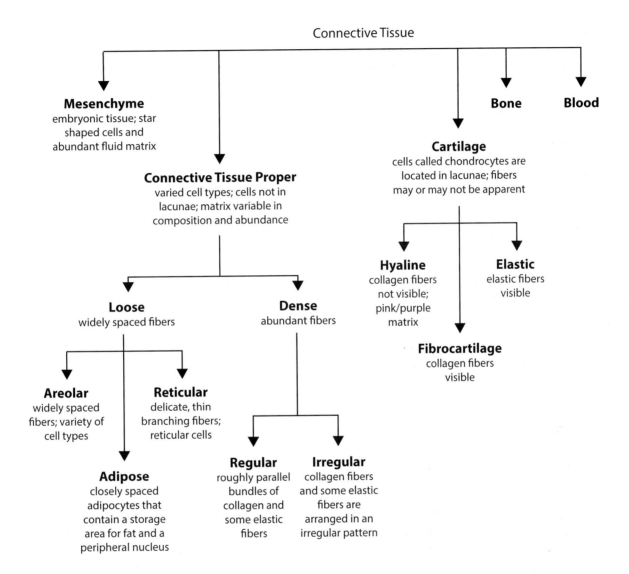

ACTIVITY 3:

Examination of Epithelial Membranes

Resources: Textbook: pages 140-142

Examine prepared slides of the following epithelial membranes under the microscope and prepare labeled sketches of each:

mucous membranes: trachea, esophagus

Tips:

1.   Epithelial membranes are simple organs that contain some type of epithelium resting on a layer of loose connective tissue.

2.   The epithelium may be stratified squamous, simple columnar, or pseudostratified columnar with cilia.

Checklist:

A.   Epithelial Tissues:

_____ simple squamous epithelium

_____ simple cuboidal epithelium

_____ simple columnar epithelium

_____ pseudostratified columnar epithelium

_____ stratified squamous epithelium

_____ stratified cuboidal epithelium

_____ stratified columnar epithelium

_____ transitional epithelium

B.   Connective Tissues:

_____ mesenchyme

_____ areolar connective tissue

_____ adipose tissue

_____ reticular tissue

_____ dense regular connective tissue

_____ dense irregular connective tissue

_____ hyaline cartilage

_____ elastic cartilage

_____ fibrocartilage

C. **Epithelial Membranes:**

_____ mucous membrane: trachea

_____ mucous membrane: esophagus

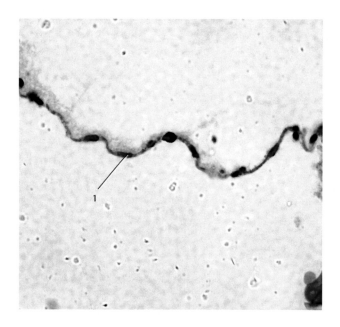

Figure 3.1: Simple squamous epithelial tissue.
1) Single layer of flattened cells.

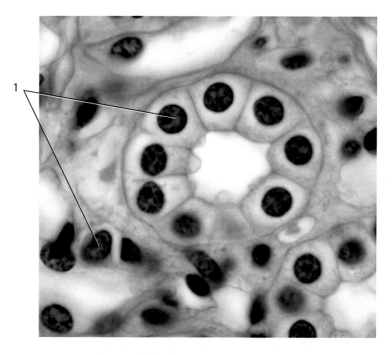

Figure 3.2: Simple cuboidal epithelial tissue.
1) Single layer of cells with round nuclei.

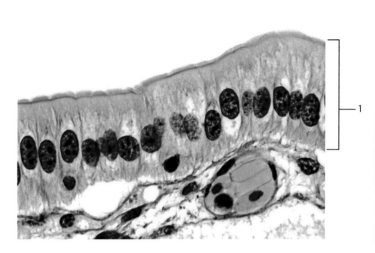

Figure 3.3: Simple columnar epithelium.
1) Single layer of cells with oval nuclei

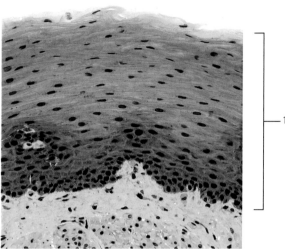

Figure 3.4: Stratified squamous epithelium.
1) Multiple layers of cells, which are flattened at the apical layer

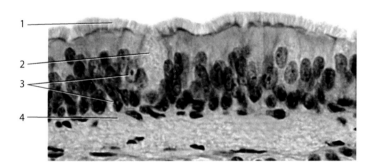

Figure 3.5: Pseudostratified columnar epithelium.
1) Cilia 2) Goblet cell 3) Pseudostratified columnar epithelium 4) Basement membrane

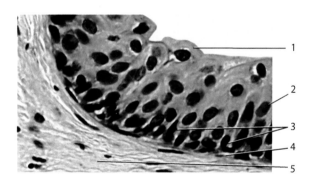

Figure 3.6: Transitional epithelium.
1) Rounder apical cell 2) Nucleus 3) Basal cells 4) Basement membrane 5) Connective tissue

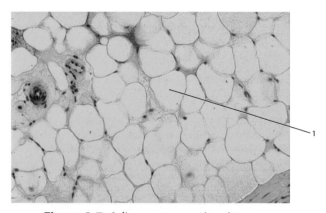

Figure 3.7: Adipose connective tissue.
1) Adipocytes (adipose cells)

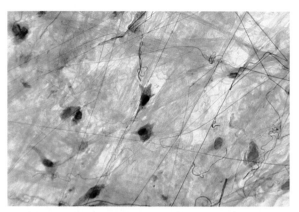

Figure 3.8: Loose areolar connective tissue.

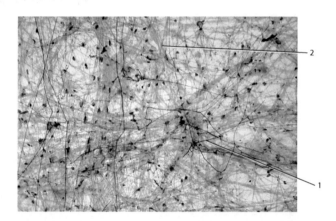

Figure 3.9: Loose areolar connective tissue stained
for fibers. 1) Elastic fibers 2) Collagen fibers

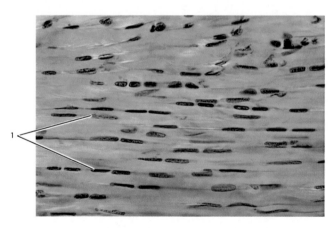

Figure 3.10: Dense regular connective tissue.
1) Nuclei of fibroblasts arranged in parallel rows

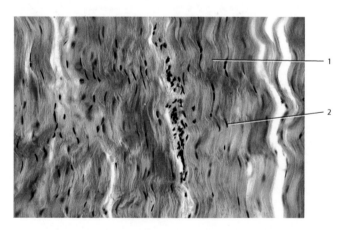

Figure 3.11: Dense regular connective tissue.
1) Collagenous fiber 2) Fibroblast

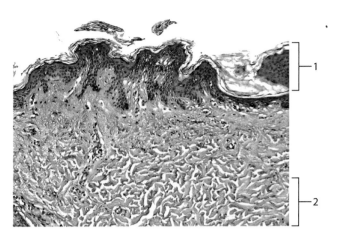

Figure 3.12: Dense irregular connective tissue.
1) Epidermis 2) Dense irregular connective tissue

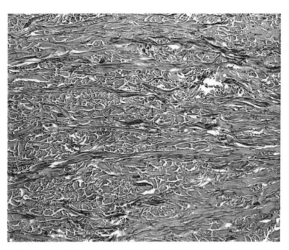

Figure 3.13: Dense irregular connective tissue.

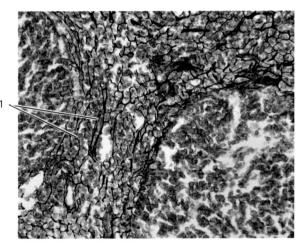

Figure 3.14: Reticular connective tissue.
1) Reticular fibers

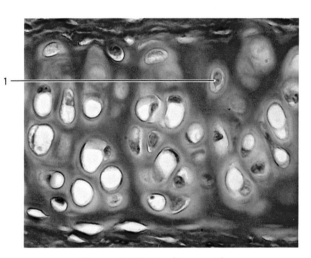

Figure 3.15: Hyaline cartilage
1) Chondrocytes

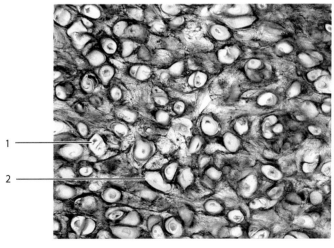

Figure 3.16: Elastic cartilage.
1) Chondrocyte 2) Lacunae

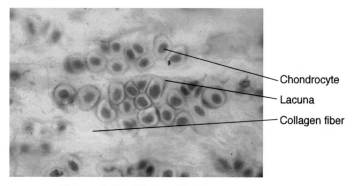

Figure 3.17: Fibrocartilage.

Chondrocyte

Lacuna

Collagen fiber

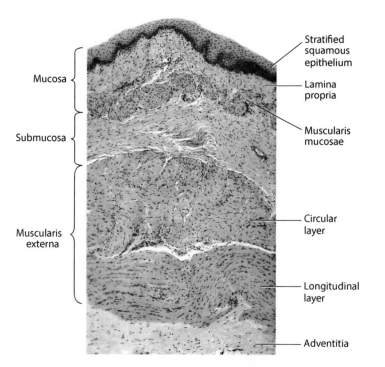

Mucosa

Submucosa

Muscularis externa

Stratified squamous epithelium

Lamina propria

Muscularis mucosae

Circular layer

Longitudinal layer

Adventitia

Figure 3.18: Cross section of the esophagus.

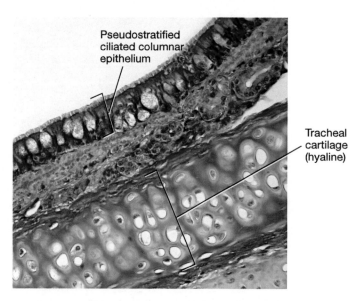

Pseudostratified ciliated columnar epithelium

Tracheal cartilage (hyaline)

Figure 3.19: Cross-section of the trachea.

Name: _____

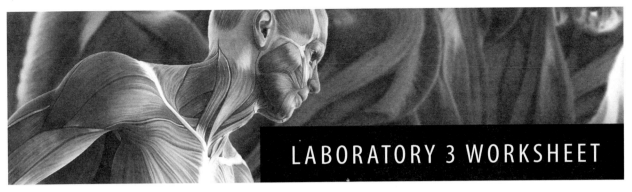

LABORATORY 3 WORKSHEET

LAB 3 WORKSHEET

Prepare labeled sketches of the following epithelial tissues **as seen under the microscope:**

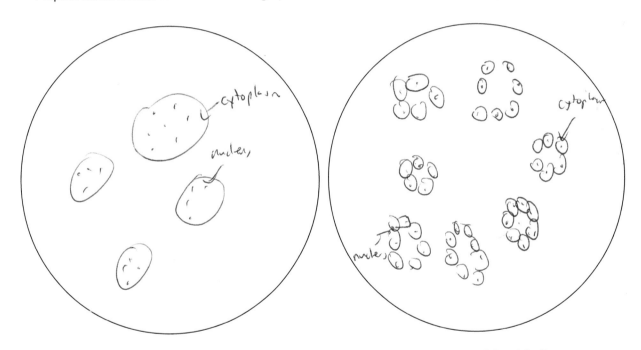

Simple Squamous Epithelium

Total magnification: _____ 40x _____
Label a nucleus, cytoplasm and
basement membrane (if visible)

Simple Cuboidal Epithelium

Total magnification: _____ 40x _____
Label a nucleus, cytoplasm and
basement membrane (if visible)

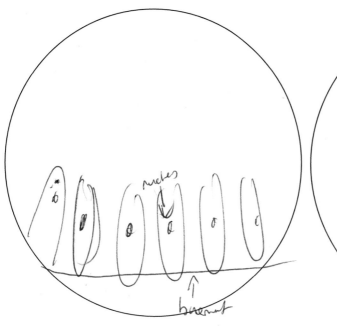

Simple Columnar Epithelium

Total Magnification: _____
Label a nucleus, cytoplasm,
basement membrane (if visible)
and goblet cell (if visible)

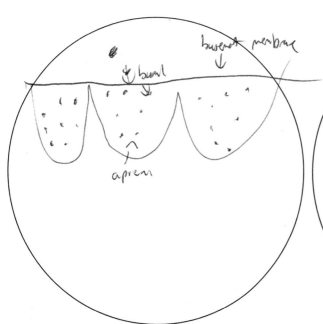

Stratified Squamous Epithelium

Total magnification: _____
Label the apical cells, the basal cells
and basement membrane (if visible)

Pseudostratified Columnar Epithelium

Total magnification: _____
Label a nucleus, cytoplasm,
basement membrane (if visible),
goblet cell (if visible) and cilia (if visible)

Transitional Epithelium

Total magnification: _____
Label the apical cells, the basal
cells and basement membrane (if visible)

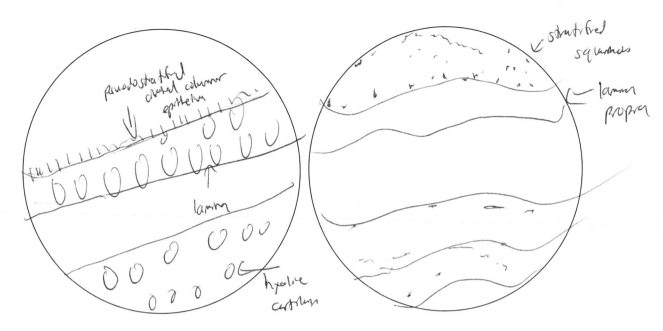

Mucous Membrane: Trachea

Total magnification: _____ 10x

Determine the type of epithelium present and label it; label the lamina propria

Mucous Membrane: Esophagus

Total magnification: _____ 10x

Determine the type of epithelium present and label it; label the lamina propria

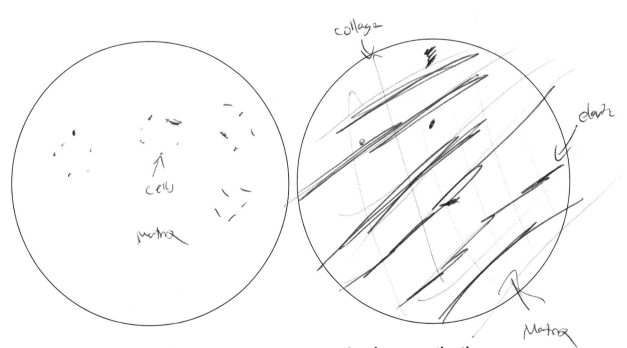

Mesenchyme

Total magnification: _____ 4x

Label the cells, matrix

Areolar connective tissue

Total magnification: _____ 4x

Label the collagen fibers, elastic fibers, matrix

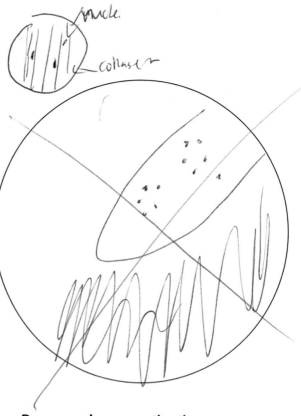

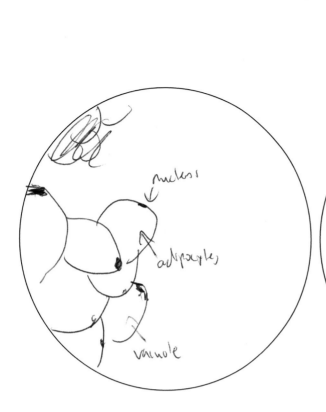

Adipose connective tissue

Total magnification: _____400x_____
Label the adipocytes, adipocyte nucleus,
and vacuole

Dense regular connective tissue

Total magnification: _____400x_____
Label the fibroblast nuclei, collagen
fibers

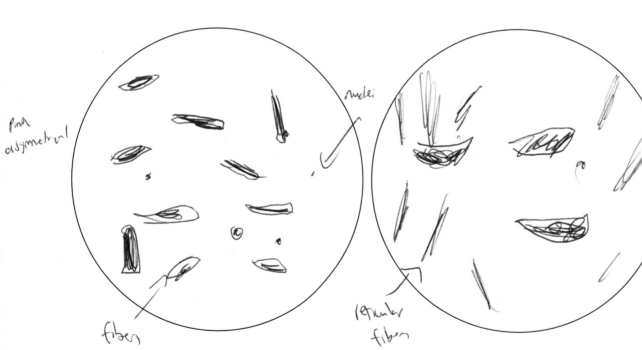

Dense irregular connective tissue

Total magnification: _____400x_____
Label the fibroblast nuclei, collagen fibers

Reticular connective tissue

Total magnification: _____400x_____
Label the reticular fibers

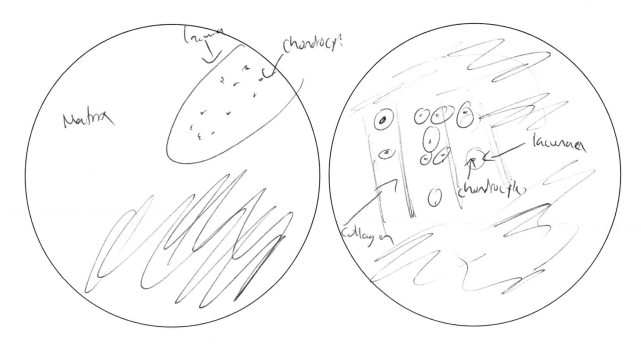

Hyaline cartilage

Total magnification: _____40x_____
Label the chondrocytes, lacuna
and matrix

Fibrocartilage

Total magnification: _____400x_____
Label the chondrocytes, lacuna
and matrix

Elastic cartilage

Total magnification: _____400x_____
Label the chondrocytes, lacuna, and matrix

POST LAB WORKSHEET LAB 3

1. List the four tissue categories:

   connective   _muscular_

   epithelial   _nervous_

2. Epithelial Tissue – Basic Structure

   Provide the appropriate term(s):

   Projections from cells used to propel
   substances over cell surfaces: _cilia_

   Term for a single layer of epithelial cells: _simple_

   The three common shapes of epithelial cells: _squamous_
                                                      cuboidal
                                                      columnar

   The two lamina of the basement membrane
   that are found between epithelial tissue and
   underlying connective tissue: _basal and reticular_

   Fingerlike extensions of the plasma
   membrane that increase surface area for cells
   involved in absorption or secretion: _microvilli_

   An epithelium with many layers: _stratified_

   Term for a single layer of epithelial cells of
   varying heights: _pseudostratified_

   Multilayered epithelium with in which the
   shape of the apical cells changes due to
   distension of the organ: _transitional_

3. Epithelium – Functions and Locations

   Match the epithelial tissue with its description. Tissues may be used more than once:

   a. stratified squamous

   b. stratified columnar

   c. stratified cuboidal

   d transitional

   e. simple squamous

   f. simple columnar

   g. simple cuboidal

   h. pseudostratified

   These two tissue types are specialized for secretion and absorption.

   _____ f, g _____

   This type of tissue is rare. It can be found in small amounts in the pharynx (throat), lining the male urethra and lining the ducts of some glands.

   _____ b _____

   This tissue permits stretching and is found lining the ureters, urethra and urinary bladder.

   _____ d _____

   This type of tissue protects deeper tissues and lines the mouth, esophagus and vagina (nonkeratinzed) and forms the epidermis of the skin (keratinized).

   _____ a _____

   This rare type of tissue often exists in two layers. It can be found in the ducts of large glands.

   _____ c _____

   This mucus-secreting tissue lines ducts of the male reproductive system (non-ciliated) and the trachea and other portions of the upper respiratory tract (ciliated).

   _____ h _____

   This tissue is specialized for filtration (kidney glomeruli) and diffusion (lungs); it lines the heart, blood vessels and lymphatic vessels and secretes fluid when found in a serous membrane.

   _____ e _____

   This tissue makes up portions of kidney tubules, the ducts and secretory portions of small glands and is found on the surface of the ovary.

   _____ g _____

   The nonciliated variety of this tissue lines portions of the digestive tract (from the stomach to the anal canal), the gall bladder and ducts of some glands; the ciliated variety lines small bronchi, uterine tubes and portions of the uterus.

   _____ f _____

4. Connective Tissue (Basic Structure), Provide the correct term(s):

The three types of fibers that can exist in connective tissue. _____ collagen, elastic, reticular

The fiber that has great tensile strength. _____ collagen

The term for embryonic connective tissue. _____ mesenchyme

Amorphous substance consisting of interstitial fluid, cell adhesion molecules and proteoglycans that fills spaces between cells. _____ ground substance

Connective tissue that consists primarily of parallel collagen fibers. _____ dense regular

Connective tissue cells that are phagocytes. _____ macrophage

Connective tissue that contains all three fiber types and has a gel like matrix. _____ areolar

Term for cells that secrete cartilage. _____ chondroblast

5. Connective Tissue – Functions and Locations.

Match the connective tissue with its description.

a. reticular tissue

b. adipose tissue

c. areolar tissue

d. dense irregular tissue

e. dense regular tissue

f. elastic cartilage

g. hyaline cartilage

h. fibrocartilage

Cartilage that has great tensile strength and is found in intervertebral discs, the symphysis pubis and discs of the knee. _____ h

Strong tissue that is found in tendons, ligaments and aponeuroses. _____ e

Strong cartilage that forms most of an embryo's skeleton, covers the ends of long bones and is associated with the ribs, nose, trachea and larynx. _____ g

Connective tissue that stores energy, protects against heat loss, and supports organs.   _____ b _____

Connective tissue that forms the internal supporting framework for lymph nodes, the spleen and bone marrow.   _____ g _____

Connective tissue that provides strength even when forces are exerted in many directions; it forms the capsules of joints, the dermis of the skin and the submucosa of the digestive tract.   _____ e _____

This flexible cartilage is used to maintain the shape of structures such as the external ear and the epiglottis of the larynx (voice box).   _____ f _____

This connective tissue is abundant deep to the skin, in the abdomen, in breasts and around the kidneys and eyes.   _____ b _____

This connective tissue is found deep to epithelial tissue; it wraps around organs and capillaries, holds fluid and contains phagocytes which destroy bacteria.   _____ c _____

6. Epithelial Membranes

    a. What type of epithelial tissue is found in mucous membranes?

    _____

    b. Where are mucous membranes found in the body?

    _____

    c. What type of epithelium is found in serous membranes?

    _____

    d. Where are serous membranes found in the body?

    _____

    e. What type of connective tissue is found deep to the epithelium in all epithelial membranes?

    _____

    f. What is a lamina propria?

    _____

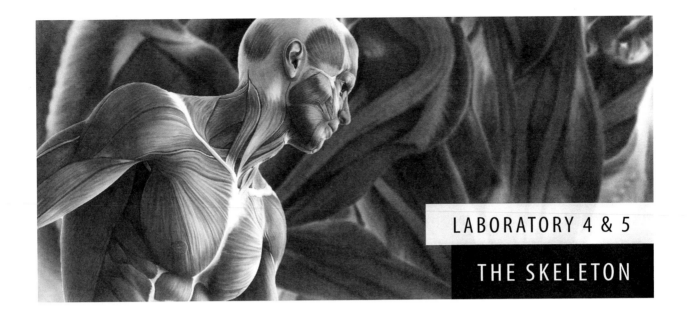

Objectives

1. Identify and classify the human bone as either long, flat, short, irregular or sesamoid

2. Define the following terms and find examples of each of these markings using bones available in the lab

foramen	trochanter	crest	tubercle
epicondyle	spine	head	line
meatus	facet	condyle	ramus
fissure	groove	sinus	fossa
tuberosity	process		

3. Describe the gross structure of a long bone and identify the different parts of a long bone using a diagram or a sectioned specimen

Diaphysis	epiphysis	periosteum	endosteum
epiphyseal line	red marrow	yellow marrow	trabeculae
articular cartilage	epiphyseal plate	perforating (Sharpey's) fibers	

4. Describe the chemical composition of a bone

5. Describe the microscopic structure of a compact bone and identify the following components of an osteon using a prepared slide, model or a diagram

central canal	lamella (concentric)	perforating canal
canaliculi	lacunae	interstitial lamella

6. Identify the following bones and their markings in the axial skeleton using specimens, models and diagrams

   a. Cranium: frontal, parietal, occipital, temporal, ethmoid, sphenoid, and sutures

   b. Facial bones: mandible, maxillae, palatine, vomer, zygomatic, nasal, lacrimal, inferior nasal conchae

   c. Hyoid bone

7. The vertebral column: cervical, thoracic, lumbar vertebrae, sacrum and coccyx

8. Thorax: sternum, ribs

9. Identify the four curvatures of the vertebral column (cervical, thoracic, lumbar, and sacral)

10. Identify the following bones and their markings in the appendicular skeleton using models, specimens and diagrams

   a. pectoral girdle and upper extremity: clavicle, scapula, humerus, radius, ulna, carpals, metacarpals, phalanges

   b. pelvic girdle and lower extremity: ilium, ischium, pubis, femur, tibia, fibula, tarsals, metatarsals, phalanges

11. Identify the foramina that act as passageways for each of the cranial nerves, spinal cord, internal carotid artery, and the internal jugular vein.

12. Identify the bones as to whether they belong to the right side or left side of the body.

INTRODUCTION

The skeletal system supports and protects the body, provides a site for blood cell formation, and is a site of mineral storage. It is made of bones that connect together to form joints. There are about 206 named bones that make up the **axial** and **appendicular skeleton**. Axial skeleton includes the bones of the skull, vertebral column and rib cage. Appendicular skeleton includes the bones of the upper and lower limbs and the pelvic and pectoral girdles. This lab exercise will focus on the study and identification of the individual bone and selected bone surface markings.

Bones can be classified as **compact** or **spongy** based on the type of osseous tissue. Compact bone is found on the hard external layer while spongy or cancellous bone is found in the interior (honey –combed appearance) Bones can also be classified as **long, short, flat** or **irregular** based on their shape.

The long bone is usually used as a sample to study the gross structure of a bone as it contains all the general features of any bone. It is used to study the microscopic structures as well. Although compact bone appears solid to the human eye, microscopically it has lot of passageways for blood vessels, nerves and lymphatic vessels. The structural unit of a compact bone is called the **osteon** or the **Haversian system**. This lab exercise will give ample opportunities to identify and classify individual bones into the different types based on shape. It will also focus on the gross structure, microscopic structure and chemical composition of bone as well.

Materials

1. Each student should have a compound microscope.

2. Class materials to be shared by students:

   Prepared slides of bone (compact, cancellous), disarticulated bones, long bone sectioned longitudinally. A bone soaked in an acidic solution and a bone which has been baked.

ACTIVITY 1:

Bone Classification

Resources: Textbook: pages 174–176

Given any human bone, classify it as being long, short, irregular, flat, or sesamoid

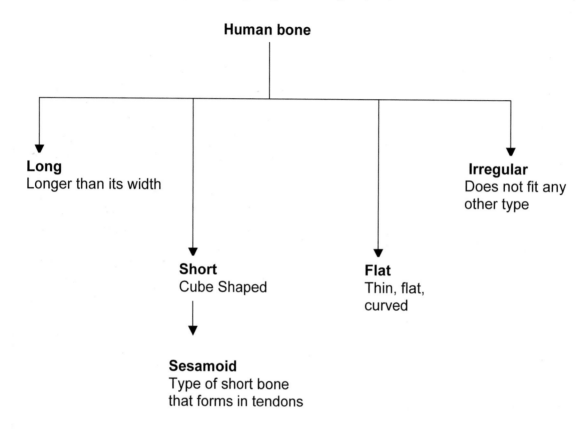

Tips:

1. To differentiate certain long bones (hand, foot) from a short bone it is helpful to look at the general characteristics as opposed to how it appears to the human eye (e.g.: metacarpals are classified as long bones even though they appear short compared to other long bones like the femur or tibia).

ACTIVITY 2:

Bone Markings

Resources: Textbook: pages 179–180

Learn the following terms and find examples of each of these markings using bones available in the laboratory.

Foramen (hole for vessels and nerves)	**Trochanter** (large, irregular, rough projection)	**Crest** (prominent ridge of bone)	**Tubercle** (smaller projection than tuberosity)
Epicondyle (area above condyle) epi=above	**spine** (sharp pointed projection)	**head** (rounded projection on top of a narrow neck)	**line** (narrow ridge of bone, less prominent than crest)
Meatus (tube like passageway)	**Facet** (smooth surface for articulation)	**Condyle** (rounded area for articulation)	**Ramus** (the portion of the bone that makes an angle with the rest of the structure)
Fissure (narrow crack or slit like opening)	**Groove** (sulcus, elongated depression in a bone)	**Sinus** (air filled cavity within a bone)	**Fossa** (shallow depressed area of a bone)
Tuberosity (large, raised, rough area)	**Process** (projection)		

Tips:

1. Most often structures passing through the different bone markings will bear a similar name as the marking. (e.g.: carotid artery passes through carotid canal; optic nerve passes through optic foramen)

2. It makes it easier to learn the above-mentioned bone markings when you categorize most of them into different groups. One suggested method is on the next page:

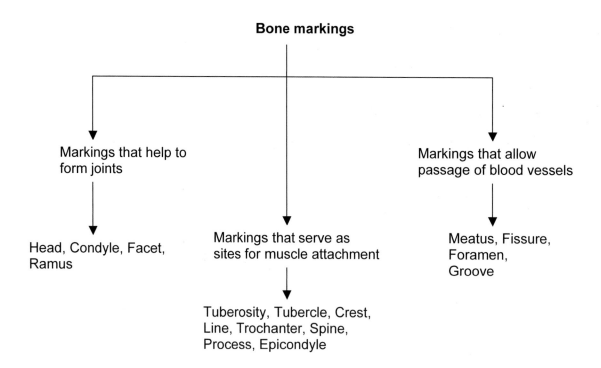

Bone markings

Markings that help to form joints
→ Head, Condyle, Facet, Ramus

Markings that serve as sites for muscle attachment
→ Tuberosity, Tubercle, Crest, Line, Trochanter, Spine, Process, Epicondyle

Markings that allow passage of blood vessels
→ Meatus, Fissure, Foramen, Groove

ACTIVITY 3:

Gross anatomy of a long bone

Resources: Textbook: pages 177-179

Identify the following portions of a long bone using a diagram or a sectioned long bone:

diaphysis	epiphysis	periosteum	endosteum
epiphyseal line	red marrow	yellow marrow	trabeculae
articular cartilage	epiphyseal plate	perforating (Sharpey's) fibers	

1. If you are using a freshly sectioned bone, proper sanitary precautions have to be followed. At the end of the activity replace the specimen in the appropriate container and dispose of the gloves in the designated place. Wash your hands before continuing other work.

2. With a fresh specimen, if you pull away the periosteum from the bone, you can see fibers extending from the periosteum to the bone. These are the Sharpey's fibers.

ACTIVITY 4:

Chemical composition of bone

Resources: Textbook: pages 182-183

Discuss the role of organic materials (collagen) and inorganic materials (minerals) in maintaining the strength of bone.

1. Observe the effects of acid and heat on a bone sample. Samples have already been pre-soaked in acid as well as baked (heat-treated).

2. Observe what happens when you apply gentle pressure to both samples. What do you think happens to the bone when it is soaked in acid and when it Is heat treated?

ACTIVITY 5:

Microscopic structure of compact bone

Resources: Textbook: pages 181-182

Identify the following portions of the osteon (Haversian system) using a prepared slide, model or diagram:

Central (Haversian) canal	perforating (Volkmann's) canal	lacunae
Canaliculi	interstitial lamellae	lamellae

Tips:

1. In the prepared slide of compact bone (ground bone) you would see rings of (concentric) lamellae around a central canal. The central canal will appear either clear or black. The osteocytes (bone cells) will also appear black. Sometimes you can see a clear space or a cavity around the osteocytes which would be the lacunae. The canaliculi appear as thin wavy threads extending from one osteocyte to another.

ACTIVITY 6:

Axial Skeleton

Resources: Textbook: pages 199-226

Identify the following bones and their markings using charts, diagrams, models and bone specimens

1. The Cranium

    a. Frontal Bone: supraorbital foramen, glabella

    b. Parietal Bone

    c. Temporal Bone: squamous region, tympanic region, mastoid region, petrous region, zygomatic process, mandibular fossa, external auditory meatus, styloid process, mastoid process, jugular foramen, carotid canal, internal acoustic meatus, foramen lacerum, stylomastoid foramen

    d. Occipital Bone: foramen magnum, occipital condyle, hypoglossal canal, external occipital crest, superior and inferior nuchal line

    e. Sphenoid Bone: greater wings, lesser wings, superior orbital fissure, sella turcica, hypophyseal fossa, optic canal, pterygoid process, foramen rotundum, foramen ovale, foramen spinosum

    f. Ethmoid Bone: crista galli, cribriform plate, perpendicular plate, superior nasal conchae, middle nasal conchae

    g. Sutures: sagittal, coronal, lambdoidal, squamosal, frontonasal

2. Facial Bones

    a. Mandible: body, ramus, mandibular condyle, coronoid process, mandibular angle, alveolar margin, mandibular foramen

    b. Maxillae: alveolar margin, palatine process, infraorbital foramen

    c. Palatine Bones

    d. Zygomatic Bones

    e. Lacrimal Bones

    f. Nasal Bones

    g. Inferior Nasal Conchae

    h. Vomer

3. Hyoid Bone: greater horn, lesser horn

4. Vertebral Column

   a. Identify the cervical, thoracic and lumbar vertebrae and indicate the number of vertebrae in each class.

   b. Identify the atlas, axis and the odontoid process (dens)

   c. Identify the sacrum, and locate the following sacral markings: superior articular process, body, alae, sacral canal, sacral promontory, median sacral crest, sacral foramina

   d. Identify the coccyx

   e. Identify the following vertebral markings: spinous process, transverse process, superior/ inferior articular process, pedicle, body, lamina, transverse foramen, vertebral foramen, costal facet, inferior notch

   f. Identify the four curvatures of the vertebral column (cervical, thoracic, lumbar, and sacral). State whether the curvature is concave or convex.

5. Bony Thorax

   a. Sternum: Manubrium, body (gladiolus), xiphoid process, jugular notch, sternal angle

   b. Ribs: True (vertebrosternal), false (vertebrocostal), floating (vertebral)

ACTIVITY 7:

Appendicular Skeleton

Resources: Textbook: pages 227-243

Identify the following bones and their markings, using charts, diagrams, models and bone specimens. Be sure to know the distinguishing features that would enable you to distinguish a right-sided bone from a left-sided bone (e.g.: be able to distinguish left humerus from right humerus).

1. The pectoral girdle and the upper extremity

   a. Clavicle: Sternal (medial) end, acromial (lateral) end

   b. Scapula: glenoid cavity, coracoid process, acromian process, medial (vertebral) border, lateral (axillary) border, superior border, inferior angle, supraspinous fossa, infraspinous fossa, subscapular fossa, suprascapular notch, spine

   c. Humerus: head, greater tubercle, lesser tubercle, intertubercular groove, anatomical neck, deltoid tuberosity, capitulum, trochlea, medial epicondyle, lateral epicondyle, coronoid fossa, olecranon fossa

   d. Radius: head, neck, radial tuberosity, ulnar notch, styloid process

   e. Ulna: olecranon process, coronoid process, styloid process, head, trochlear notch, radial notch

   f. Carpals: scaphoid, lunate, triquetral, pisiform, trapezium, trapezoid, capitate, hamate

g. Metacarpals and Phalanges

2. The pelvic girdle and lower extremity

   a. Ilium: Iliac crest, anterior superior iliac spine, anterior inferior iliac spine, posterior superior iliac spine, posterior inferior iliac spine, greater sciatic notch, iliac fossa

   b. Ischium: Ischial tuberosity, ischial spine, lesser sciatic notch, ischial ramus

   c. Pubis: crest, inferior ramus

   d. Define the term "os coxae"

   e. Identify the obturator foramen and acetabulum

   f. Identify the features that distinguish a male and a female pelvis

   g. Femur: head, neck, greater trochanter, lesser trochanter, intertrochanteric crest, intertrochanteric line, linea aspera, lateral condyle, medial condyle, gluteal tuberosity, lateral epicondyle, medial epicondyle, patellar surface, adductor tubercle

   h. Tibia: medial condyle, lateral condyle, intercondylar eminence, tibial tuberosity, medial malleolus

   i. Fibula: lateral malleolus, head

   j. Tarsals: Calcaneus, Talus, navicular, cuboid, lateral cuneiform, medial cuneiform, intermediate cuneiform

   k. Patella

Tips:

1. The following steps could be helpful in distinguishing whether a bone is from the left or the right side of the body:

   a. Identify the bone

   b. Pick bone markings that will help you distinguish the anterior portion from the posterior portion of the bone

   c. Pick important bone markings to distinguish the medial side of the bone from the lateral side of the bone

   d. Identify the superior and inferior surface of the bone

   e. Putting all these features together will help you correctly identify the side of the body that a bone comes from.

   f. Example: In the femur, the anterior surface is smooth and curved, while the posterior surface is rough. The superior part has a rounded head (which forms the hip joint with the hip bone). So, the head has to be medial, or towards the center of the body. The inferior surface has a smooth articular surface with the knee cap (patella). The greater trochanter will be always be on the lateral side. Combining all these features will help you orient a femur in the lab.

ACTIVITY 8:

Structures and their foramina

Resources: Textbook: pages 202-212 (table 7.1, page 216)

Identify the foramina that act as passageways for each of the twelve cranial nerves, the internal carotid artery and the internal jugular vein.

Tips:

1. Most often structures passing through the different bone markings will bear a similar name as the marking. (e.g.: internal jugular vein passes through jugular foramen; hypoglossal nerve passes through hypoglossal canal)

Checklist:

_____ classification of bones based on shape

_____ bone surface markings

_____ gross structure of bone

_____ chemical composition of bone

_____ microscopic structure of compact bone

_____ axial skeleton

_____ Skull

_____ facial bones

_____ vertebral column

_____ bony thorax

_____ hyoid bone

_____ cranial sutures

_____ appendicular skeleton

_____ Clavicle

_____ scapula

_____ humerus

_____ ulna

_____ radius

_____ carpals

_____ metacarpals and phalanges

_____ os coxae

_____ femur

_____ tibia

_____ fibula

_____ tarsals

_____ metatarsals and phalanges

_____ distinguishing between right-sided and left-sided bones

_____ 12 cranial nerves, carotid artery, internal jugular vein and their foramina

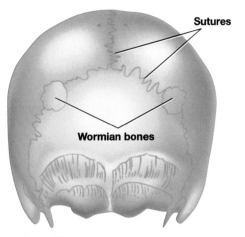

Sutures

Wormian bones

Sutural bones
- also called Wormian bones
- small, flat bones found within the skull sutures
- high degree of individual variation in number and size

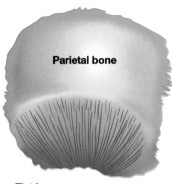

Parietal bone

Flat bones
- thin like a plate
- protect underlying structures
- large surface area for tendon and ligament attachments
- examples are cranial bones, sternum, ribs, and scapula

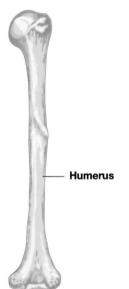

Humerus

Long bones
- longer than wide
- most common type of bone
- range from very large femur to small phalangeal bones

Patella

Sesamoid bones
- small, short bones
- develop inside tendons
- presence of other sesamoid bones is highy variable

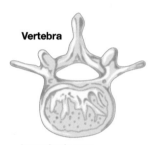

Vertebra

Irregular bones
- complex shape with notches and processes
- example are the vertebrae

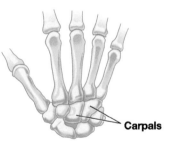

Carpals

Short bones
- similar length and width
- roughly cube-shaped
- examples are carpals and tarsals

Figure 4 & 5.1: Classification of bones based on shape.

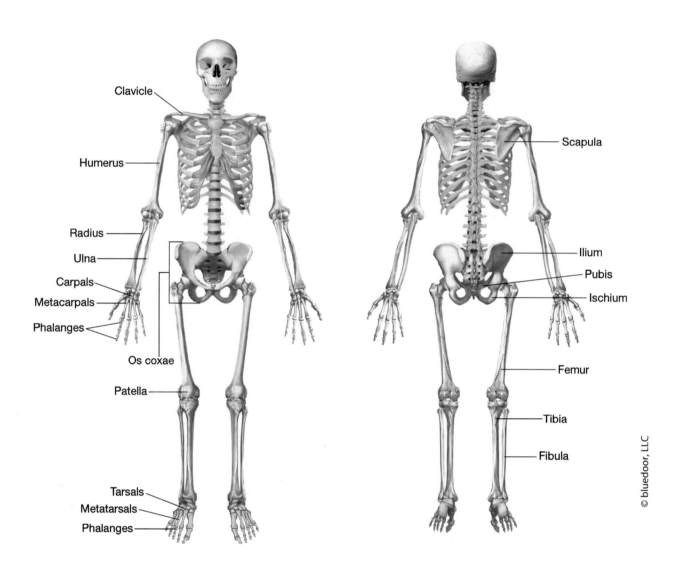

Figure 4 & 5.2: Anterior and posterior view of the skeleton.

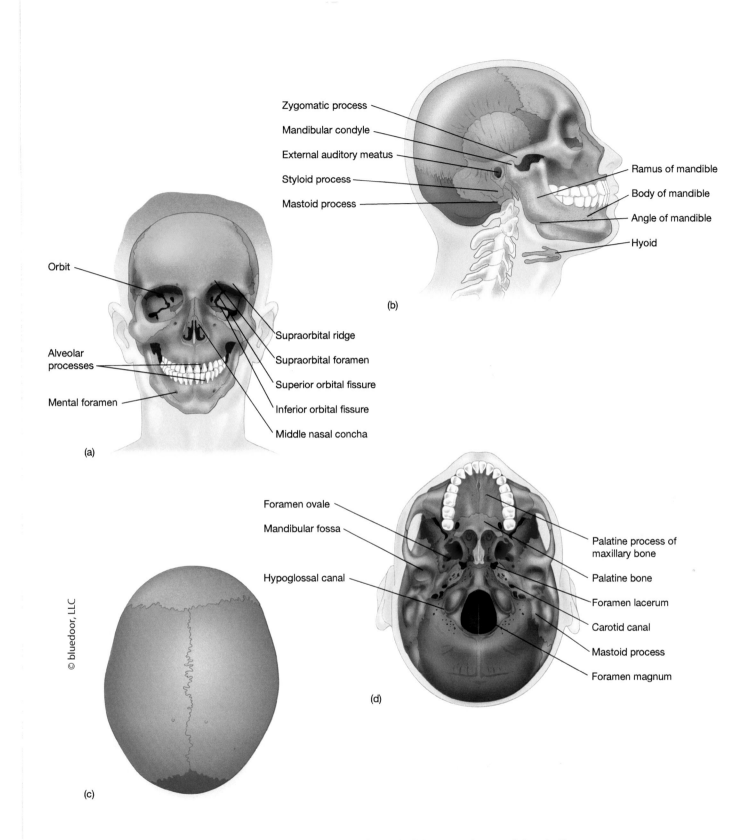

© bluedoor, LLC

Figure 4 & 5.3: a) Anterior view of the skull b) Lateral view of the skull
c) Superior view of the skull d) Inferior view of the skull

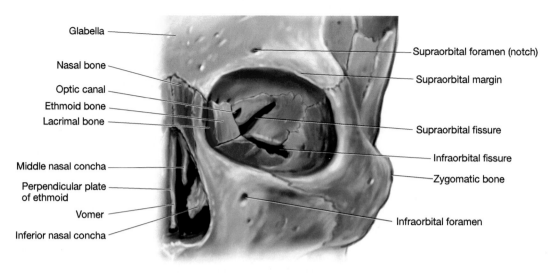

Figure 4 & 5.4: The orbit of the skull

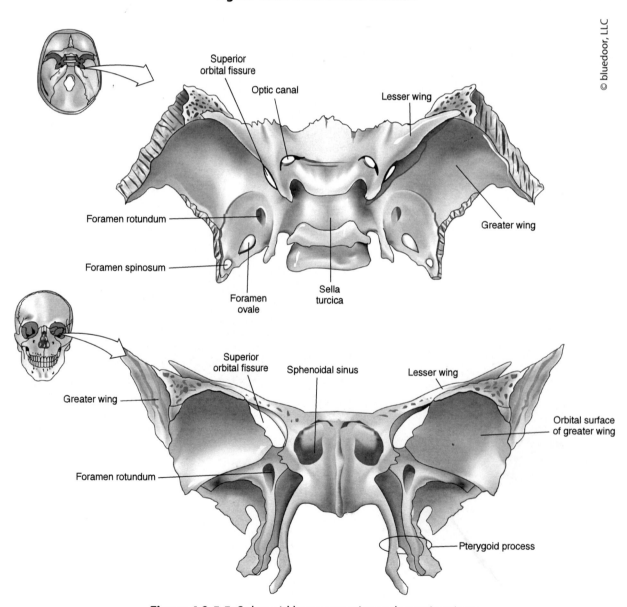

Figure 4 & 5.5: Sphenoid bone, superior and anterior views

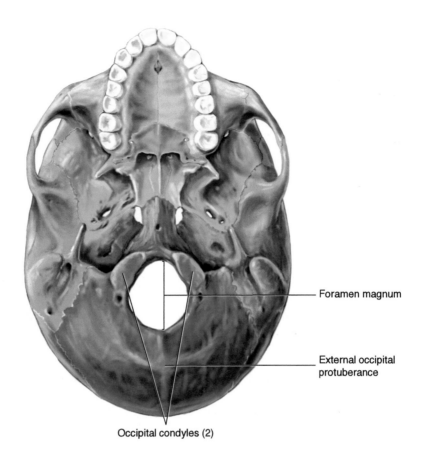

Foramen magnum

External occipital protuberance

Occipital condyles (2)

Figure 4 & 5.6: Inferior view of the occipital bone

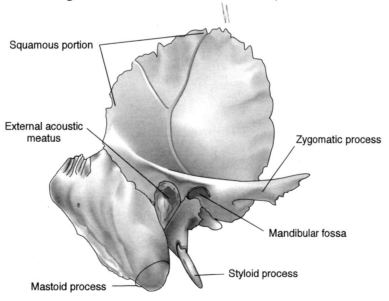

Squamous portion

External acoustic meatus

Zygomatic process

Mandibular fossa

Styloid process

Mastoid process

Figure 4 & 5.7: Lateral view of the temporal bone

© bluedoor, LLC

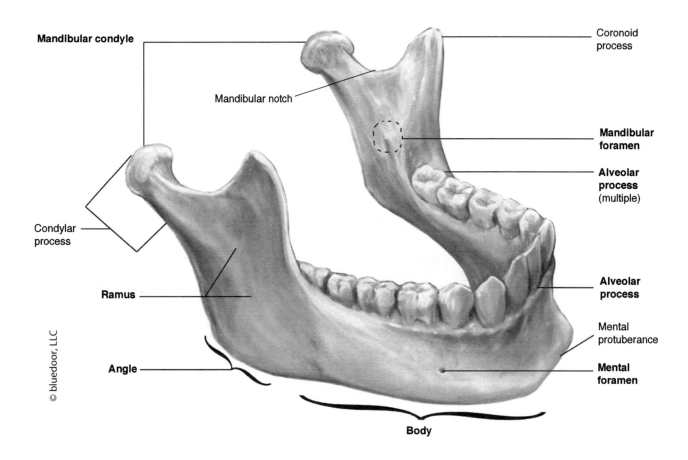

Figure 4 & 5.8: Mandible, anterolateral view

Mandibular condyle

Mandibular notch

Coronoid process

Mandibular foramen

Alveolar process (multiple)

Condylar process

Ramus

Alveolar process

Mental protuberance

Angle

Mental foramen

Body

© bluedoor, LLC

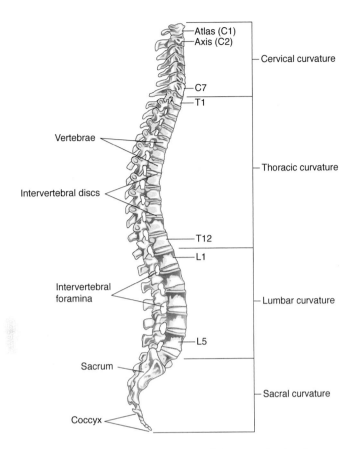

Figure 4 & 5.9: The curvature of the vertebral column

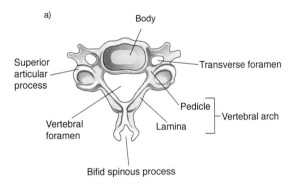

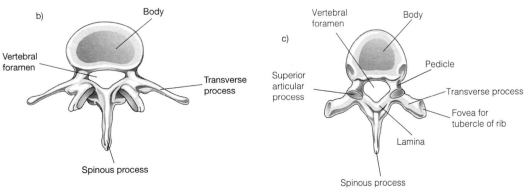

Figure 4 & 5.10: a) Cervical vertebra b) Lumbar vertebra c) Thoracic vertebra

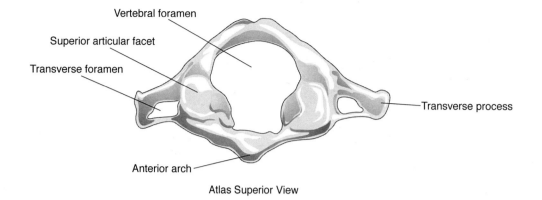

Vertebral foramen

Superior articular facet

Transverse foramen

Transverse process

Anterior arch

Atlas Superior View

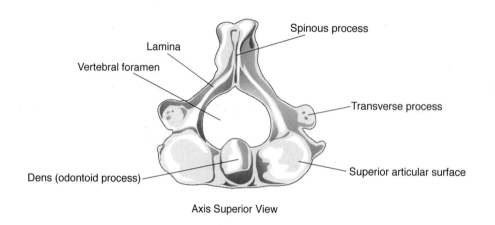

Spinous process

Lamina

Vertebral foramen

Transverse process

Dens (odontoid process)

Superior articular surface

Axis Superior View

Figure 4 & 5.11: Superior views of the atlas and the axis

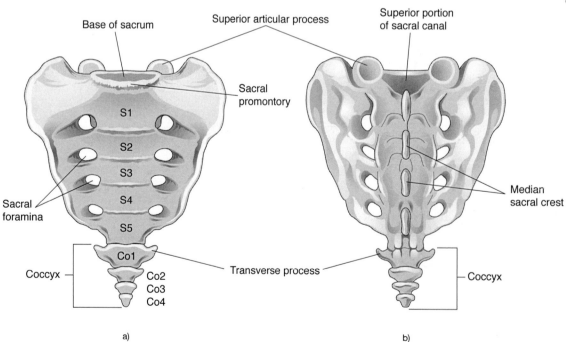

Base of sacrum

Superior articular process

Superior portion of sacral canal

Sacral promontory

S1

S2

S3

S4

S5

Co1

Co2
Co3
Co4

Sacral foramina

Coccyx

Transverse process

Median sacral crest

Coccyx

a)

b)

Figure 4 & 5.12: a) Anterior view of the sacrum and coccyx
b) Posterior view of the sacrum and coccyx

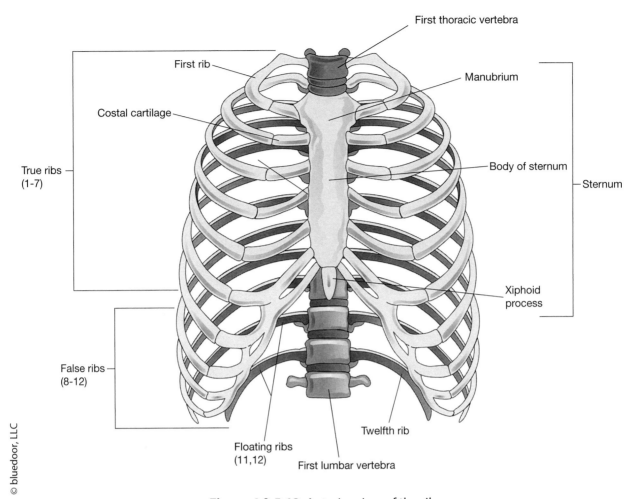

First thoracic vertebra

First rib

Costal cartilage

True ribs
(1-7)

Manubrium

Body of sternum

Sternum

Xiphoid
process

False ribs
(8-12)

Floating ribs
(11,12)

First lumbar vertebra

Twelfth rib

© bluedoor, LLC

Figure 4 & 5.13: Anterior view of the rib cage

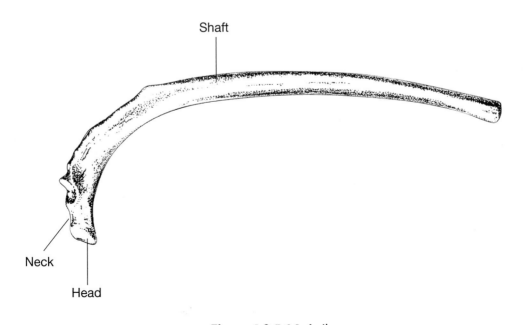

Shaft

Neck

Head

Figure 4 & 5.14: A rib

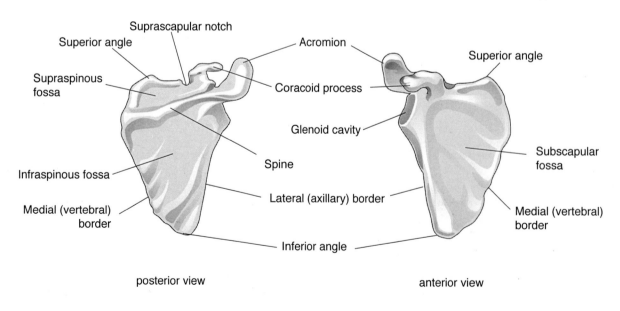

Figure 4 & 5.15: Sections of a long bone showing the outer compact bone and inner spongy bone

Spongy bone

Compact bone

Blood vessel

Medullary cavity

perforating (Sharpey's) fibers

Periosteum

Endosteum

Epiphyseal line

Articular cartilage

Proximal epiphysis

Diaphysis

Distal epiphysis

Articular cartilage

Suprascapular notch

Superior angle

Supraspinous fossa

Infraspinous fossa

Medial (vertebral) border

Acromion

Coracoid process

Glenoid cavity

Spine

Lateral (axillary) border

Inferior angle

Superior angle

Subscapular fossa

Medial (vertebral) border

posterior view

anterior view

Figure 4 & 5.16: Anterior & posterior view of the right scapula

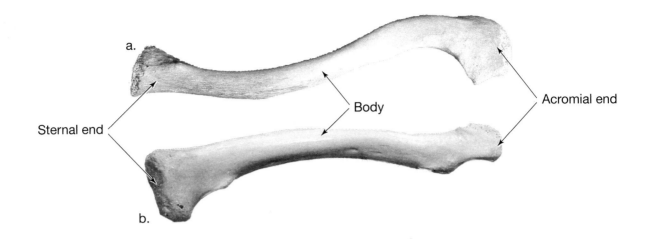

a.

Sternal end

Body

Acromial end

b.

Figure 4 & 5.17: Anterior and posterior view of the clavicle

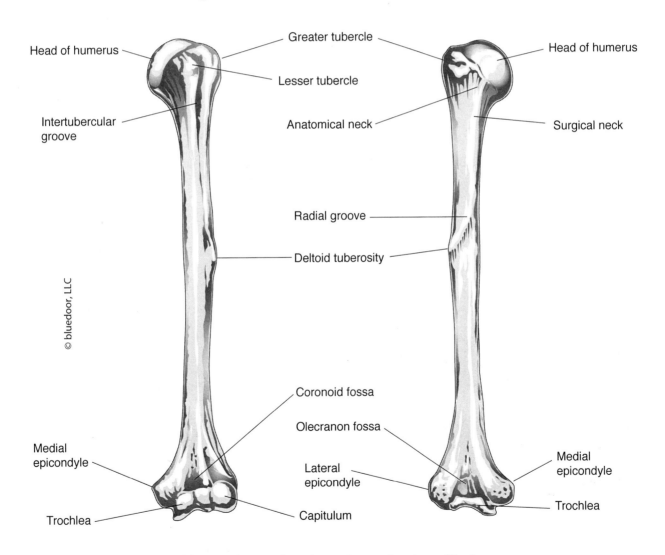

Head of humerus

Greater tubercle

Head of humerus

Lesser tubercle

Intertubercular groove

Anatomical neck

Surgical neck

Radial groove

Deltoid tuberosity

© bluedoor, LLC

Coronoid fossa

Olecranon fossa

Medial epicondyle

Lateral epicondyle

Medial epicondyle

Trochlea

Capitulum

Trochlea

Figure 4 & 5.18: Anterior and posterior view of the humerus

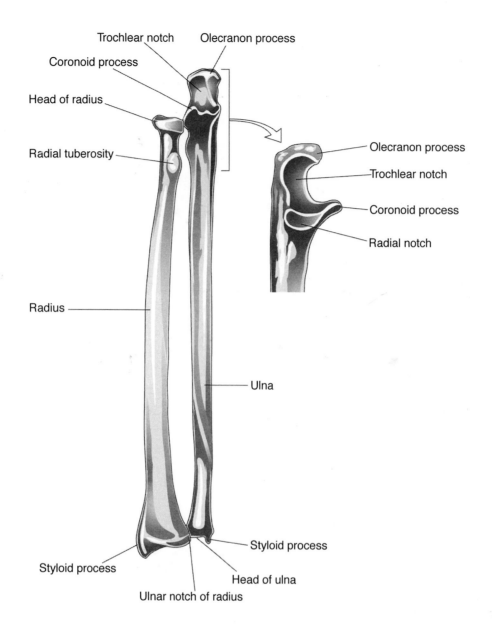

Trochlear notch   Olecranon process
Coronoid process
Head of radius
Radial tuberosity

Olecranon process
Trochlear notch
Coronoid process
Radial notch

Radius

Ulna

Styloid process

Styloid process
Head of ulna
Ulnar notch of radius

Figure 4 & 5.19: Ulna and radius

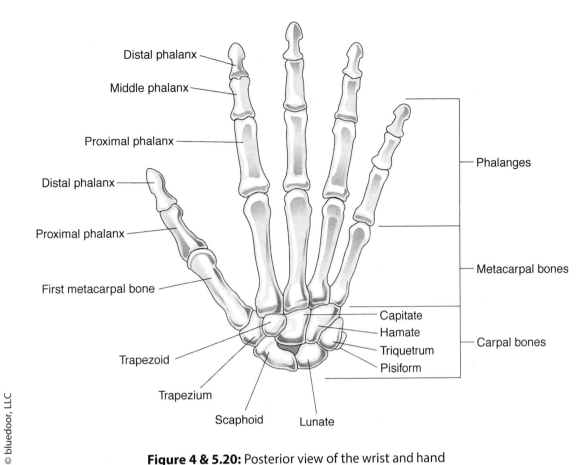

© bluedoor, LLC

Figure 4 & 5.20: Posterior view of the wrist and hand

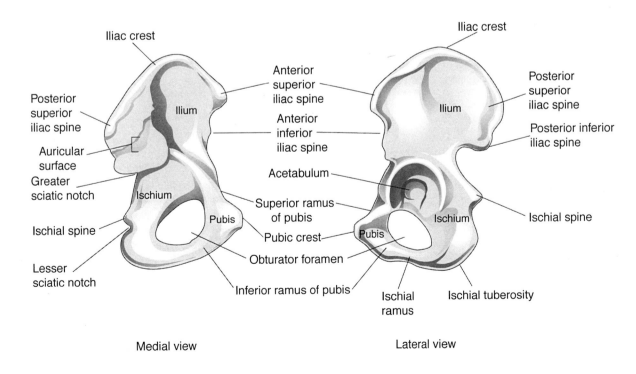

Medial view

Lateral view

Figure 4 & 5.21: Medial and lateral view of the pelvic girdle

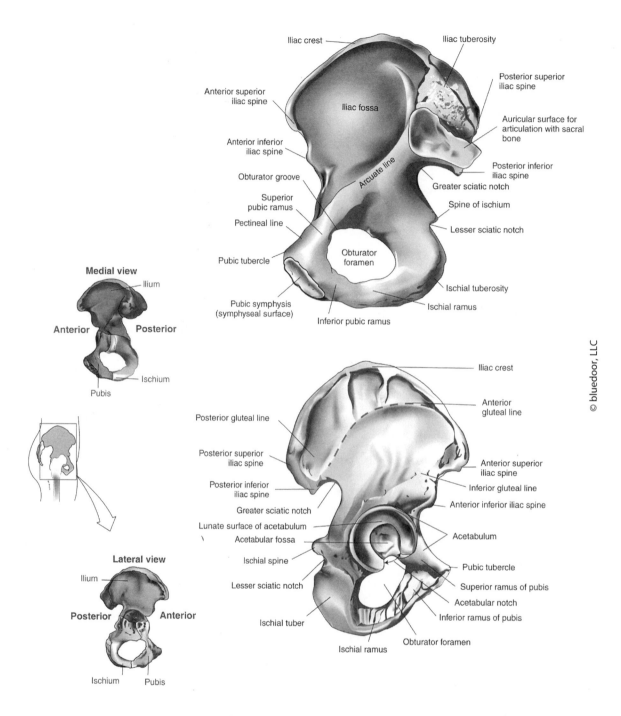

Figure 4 & 5.22: Medial and lateral view of the os coxae

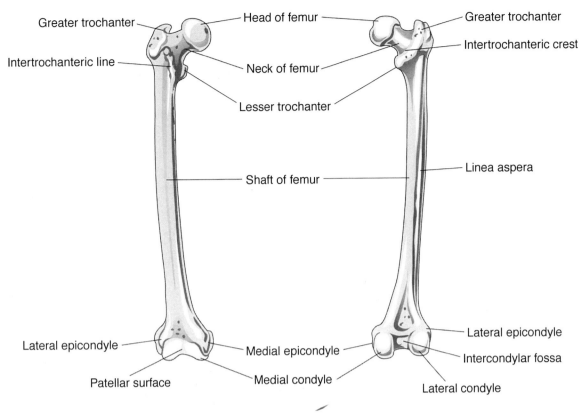

Greater trochanter

Head of femur

Greater trochanter

Intertrochanteric line

Neck of femur

Intertrochanteric crest

Lesser trochanter

Shaft of femur

Linea aspera

Lateral epicondyle

Medial epicondyle

Lateral epicondyle

Intercondylar fossa

Patellar surface

Medial condyle

Lateral condyle

© bluedoor, LLC

Figure 4 & 5.23: The femur

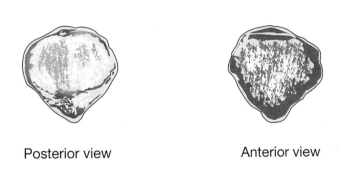

Posterior view

Anterior view

Figure 4 & 5.24: Posterior and anterior view of the patella

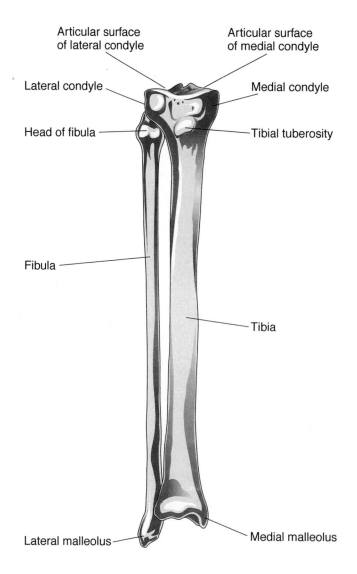

Articular surface
of lateral condyle

Articular surface
of medial condyle

Lateral condyle

Medial condyle

Head of fibula

Tibial tuberosity

Fibula

Tibia

Lateral malleolus

Medial malleolus

Figure 4 & 5.25: Anterior view of the tibia and fibula

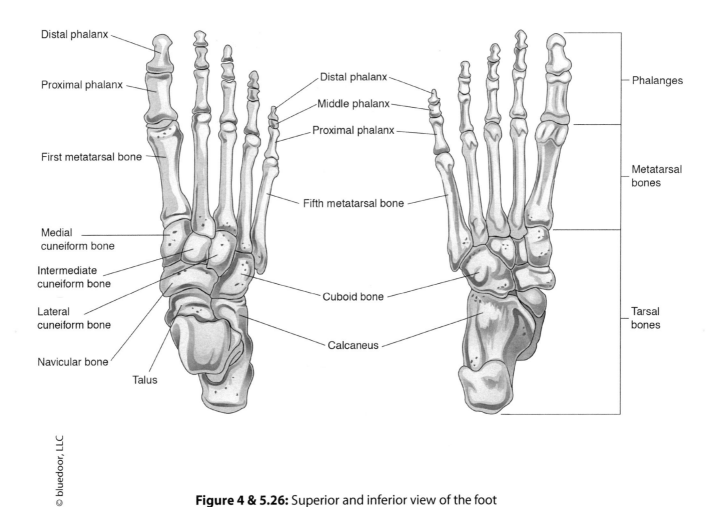

Distal phalanx

Proximal phalanx

First metatarsal bone

Medial cuneiform bone

Intermediate cuneiform bone

Lateral cuneiform bone

Navicular bone

Talus

Distal phalanx

Middle phalanx

Proximal phalanx

Fifth metatarsal bone

Cuboid bone

Calcaneus

Phalanges

Metatarsal bones

Tarsal bones

© bluedoor, LLC

Figure 4 & 5.26: Superior and inferior view of the foot

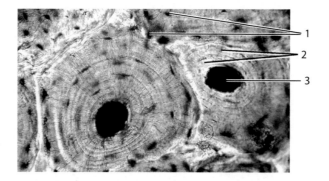

Figure 4 & 5.27: Cross-section of two osteons.
1) Lacunae 2) Lamellae 3) Central canal

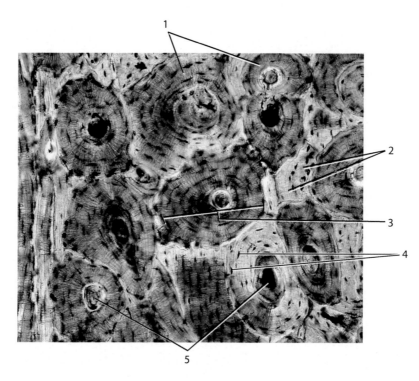

Figure 4 & 5.28: Photomicrograph of bone tissue.
1) Lamellae 2) Interstitial lamellae 3) Osteon
4) Lacunae 5) Central canal

Name: _____

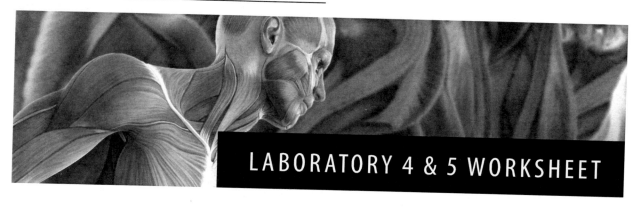

LABORATORY 4 & 5 WORKSHEET

LAB 4 AND 5 WORKSHEET

1. Classify each bone listed by checking the appropriate column

	Long	Short	Flat	Irregular
Femur	✓			
Frontal			✓	
Atlas				✓
Fibula	✓			
Sacrum				
Patella				
Talus				
Metatarsal				
Phalange				
Sternum				

2. Match the term with the appropriate description

a. facet   c. meatus   e. trochanter   g. foramen   i. epicondyle   k. spine

b. fossa   d. crest   f. sinus   h. fissure   j. condyle

_f_ Air filled cavity

_h_ Slit like opening

_____ Large rounded projection for articulation

_e_ Large irregular projection

_b_ Shallow depression

_d_ Prominent ridge of bone

_k_ Sharp slender process

_i_ Raised area above the condyle

_g_ Opening for vessels and nerves

_c_ Canal like passageway

_a_ Smooth surface for articulation

3. Use the terms to identify the structures marked by lines in the diagram.(some terms are used more than once)

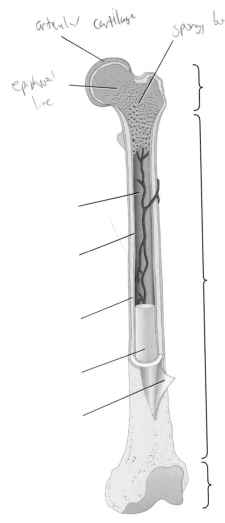

articular cartilage

spongy bone

epiphyseal line

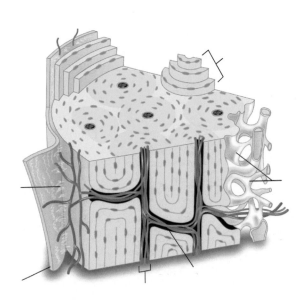

a. epiphysis
b. periosteum
c. epiphyseal line
d. endosteum
e. medullary cavity
f. compact bone
g. articular cartilage
h. trabeculae
i. diaphysis
j. perforating (Sharpey's) fibers

k. red marrow cavity
l. nutrient artery
m. yellow marrow
n. circumferential lamellae
o. concentric lamellae
p. central canal
q. Volkmann's (perforating) canal

© bluedoor, LLC

4. Use the terms from the key in question # 3 to match the statements below

_____ e _____ The adult remnant of the growth plate

_____ j _____ collagenous bundles arising from the periosteum that penetrate the bone

_____ a _____ contains spongy bone in adults

_____ i _____ the region of the bone found between the two epiphyses

_____ d _____ lines the medullary cavity

_____ g _____ hyaline cartilage found covering the epiphyses

_____ k _____ site of blood cell formation

_____ h _____ the plates of bone in spongy bone

5. What happened when gentle pressure was applied to the bone treated with acid? What does the acid appear to remove from the bone?

_____

_____

_____

6. What happened when gentle pressure was applied to the baked bone? What does baking appear to do to the bone?

_____

_____

_____

7. Which demonstration specimen (acid treated or heat treated) closely resembles a clinical disorder with bone softness?

_____

8. Prepare a sketch of ground compact bone as it appears under the microscope and label the following structures:

canaliculi, concentric lamella, lacunae, osteon, central canal, interstitial lamella, perforating (Volkmann's) canal

9. Define the following:

Canaliculi _____

_____

Lacunae _____

_____

Osteon _____

_____

Central canal _____

_____

Perforating (Volkmann's) canal _____

_____

Concentric lamella_____

_____

Interstitial lamella _____

_____

10. Rearrange the order of bones listed, to their proper order as they appear in an articulated skeleton (from cephalic to caudal end).

mandible, first metatarsal, fibula, zygomatic, parietal, talus, clavicle, twelfth thoracic vertebra, sacrum, 1st rib

Correct order of bones

_____

_____

_____

_____

_____

_____

_____

_____

_____

_____

11. Sort the following bones based on whether they belong to the appendicular or axial skeleton.

coccyx, atlas, fibula, sphenoid, radius, vomer, calcaneus, clavicle, axis, sacrum, navicular, sternum, os coxae, scapula, pisiform, ethmoid

Axial	**Appendicular**
_____	_____
_____	_____
_____	_____
_____	_____
_____	_____
_____	_____
_____	_____

12. Indicate all the structures (cranial nerve(s), artery(ies), or vein(s)) that pass through the following foramina, canals, fissures or meatus:

jugular foramen _____

carotid canal _____

internal acoustic meatus _____

foramen magnum _____

hypoglossal canal _____

optic canal _____

foramen rotundum _____

foramen ovale _____

stylomastoid foramen _____

cribriform plate _____

superior orbital fissure _____

inferior orbital fissure _____

13. Label the four curvatures of the vertebral column. Indicate whether they are convex or concave.

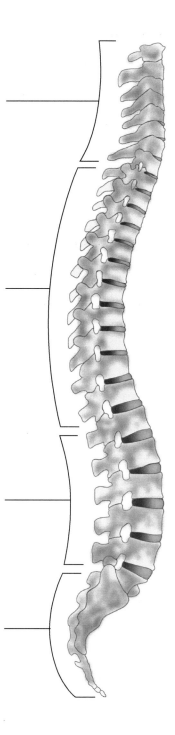

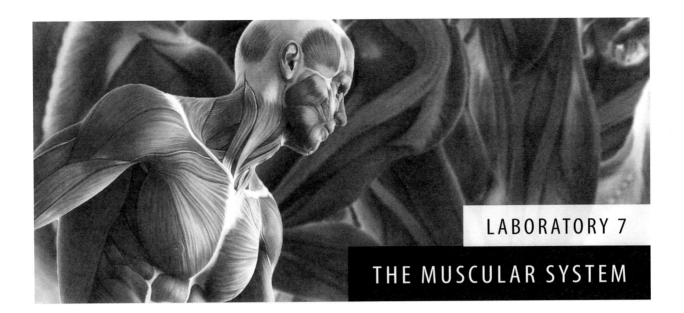

LABORATORY 7

THE MUSCULAR SYSTEM

Objectives

1. Identify the three types of muscle tissue using models, diagrams and prepared slides. Identify the following cellular structures: nucleus, sarcolemma, sarcoplasm, striations, A band, I band, intercalated discs, sarcomere, T tubules

2. Describe the function and arrangement of the connective tissue coverings of skeletal muscle. Identify the following structures using a prepared slide and/or diagram of a sectioned skeletal muscle: epimysium, perimysium, fascicle, endomysium

3. Describe the neuromuscular junction and identify the following structures using a prepared slide, model or diagram: axon terminal, motor neuron and muscle fiber

4. Identify the following human skeletal muscles using diagrams and models:

Thorax

pectoralis major	pectoralis minor	deltoid _New shoulder_	trapezius _Lateral neck to back_
respiratory diaphragm	serratus anterior	latissimus dorsi	subscapularis
external intercostals	internal intercostals	rhomboideus major	rhomboideus minor
levator scapulae	supraspinatus _Behind spine area_	infraspinatus	teres major
teres minor			

Head

frontalis	occipitalis	temporalis	mentalis
orbicularis oculi	orbicularis oris	masseter	buccinator

Neck and vertebral column

splenius	spinalis	semispinalis	longissimus
iliocostalis	sternocleidomastoid		

Upper appendage

biceps brachii *Medial arm*	triceps brachii *Lateral arm*	brachialis	brachioradialis
pronator teres	palmaris longus	supinator	flexor carpi ulnaris
flexor carpi radialis	extensor carpi radialis longus	extensor carpi ulnaris	flexor digitorum profundus
extensor carpi radialis brevis	flexor digitorum superficialis	flexor pollicis longus	extensor digitorum

Abdomen

external oblique	internal oblique	rectus abdominus	transverse abdominus

Lower appendage

gluteus maximus	gluteus medius	gluteus minimus	adductor longus
adductor brevis	adductor magnus	biceps femoris	semimembranosus
semitendinosus	rectus femoris	vastus lateralis	vastus medialis
vastus intermedius	tensor fascia latae	tibialis posterior	tibialis anterior
sartorius	gracilis	gastrocnemius	soleus
pectineus	psoas major	iliacus	extensor hallicis longus
extensor digitorum longus	flexor digitorum longus	fibularis (peroneus) longus	fibularis (peroneus) brevis

INTRODUCTION

The three types of muscle tissue are **skeletal, cardiac** and **smooth**. All three muscle types have cells with the ability to contract and relax. This contractile property helps in movement and aids in propulsion of materials through hollow organs. Each muscle tissue type differs in structure relative to its function.

Skeletal muscle attaches to and covers the skeleton and takes part in overall body movement. It is also known as voluntary muscle (consciously controlled) and as striated muscle (appearance is striped). Skeletal muscle cells are large, long, and cylindrical with multiple nuclei per cell. They have the characteristic stripes or cross striations due to the alternating arrangement of the light (I) and dark (A) bands. The myofibrils are made of myofilaments. Each myofilament contains actin and myosin (contractile proteins) which slide past each other during muscular action and bring about contraction. The sarcolemma is the plasma membrane of the long muscle fiber or muscle cell. It dips or invaginates into the interior of the cell at several points to form T tubules. Inside the sarcoplasm of the cell (cytoplasm) is the membranous network of sarcoplasmic reticulum (endoplasmic reticulum). The contractile unit of a muscle is called sarcomere, which extends from the middle of one I band to the middle of the next one.

Cardiac muscle is found in the heart. It helps in the forceful pumping of blood from the chambers of the heart into the blood vessels. Like skeletal muscle cells, cardiac muscle cells are also striated, but involuntary (not under the conscious control). They have a single nucleus, muscle fibers are branched and not tapered at the ends. They have specialized intercalated discs that attach and fuse adjacent fibers together. This prevents the separation of fibers when the heart muscle contracts forcefully as a single unit.

Smooth muscle is found in the walls of hollow visceral organs and propels food and other materials through these passageways. Like cardiac muscle cells, they are also involuntary but lack striations. They are spindle shaped cells with a single nucleus.

Individual skeletal muscle fibers, bundles of fibers and the entire muscle are enclosed by connective tissue. Each muscle fiber is enclosed by areolar connective tissue sheath called endomysium (endo= inner). Several fibers are bound together to form a fasciculus, which is covered by perimysium. The entire muscle is enclosed by epimysium, made of dense connective tissue.

Each of these individual skeletal muscle cell is stimulated to contract by a motor neuron. Together, the neuron and all the muscle cells innervated by it is known as motor unit.

Each axon divides into many branches called axon terminals, which innervate individual muscle fibers. The junction between each muscle cell and the nerve fiber is the neuromuscular junction. This lab will provide a clear understanding of the different types of muscles and their microscopic structure, connective tissue sheaths of skeletal muscle and neuromuscular junction.

Materials

1. Each student should have a compound microscope

2. Each pair of students should have:

   Prepared slides   colored pencils

   Lens paper   lens cleaner

   Immersion oil

3. Models, charts of human skeletal muscles to be shared by all students

ACTIVITY 1:

Muscular Tissues

Resources: Textbook: pages 138 –139; 310-311

Examine models and prepared slides of the following muscular tissues under the microscope and prepare labeled sketches of each one

   Skeletal muscle tissue   cardiac muscle tissue   smooth muscle tissue

Tips:

1. Note the position of the nucleus in each type of muscle tissue. In skeletal muscle tissue you will see them just beneath the cell membrane. Look closely for the striations (alternating dark and light areas perpendicular to the length of the muscle fiber).

2. Look for intercalated discs which appear as dark bands where the cardiac muscle cells connect.

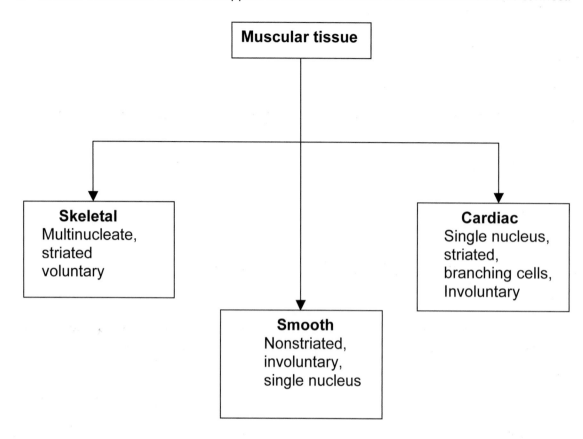

ACTIVITY 2:

Connective Tissue Sheaths

Resources: Textbook: pages 278 -279

Identify the following connective tissue sheaths of the skeletal muscle using models, diagrams and prepared slides.

Fascicle, endomysium, perimysium, and epimysium

Tips :

1. A muscle is made of bundles of muscle fibers. Each whole muscle is enclosed by epimysium (epi = outer).

2. Each whole muscle is made of bundles of muscle fibers and each bundle is called a fascicle. Each fasciculus is covered by fibrous connective tissue called perimysium. (peri=around).

3. In each bundle or fasciculus there are many individual muscle fibers and each fiber is surrounded by endomysium (endo = inner).

ACTIVITY 3:

Neuromuscular Junction

Resources: Textbook: page 294

Using prepared slides, models and diagram identify the following structures in a neuromuscular junction.

Axonal terminal   motor neuron axon   muscle fiber (cells)

ACTIVITY 4:

Identification of Human Skeletal Muscles

Resources: Textbook: pages 326 -381

Identify the following human muscles using diagrams and models. Learn the origin, insertion, action and nerve supply for each individual muscle using the muscle tables and charts provided.

Head

frontalis	occipitalis	temporalis	mentalis
orbicularis oculi Eye	orbicularis oris lips	masseter lateral cheek	buccinator medial cheek

Neck and vertebral column

splenius capitis + cervicis	spinalis Next to spine	semispinalis wder occiptalis	longissimus
iliocostalis	sternocleidomastoid		

Thorax

pectoralis major	pectoralis minor	deltoid	trapezius
respiratory diaphragm	serratus anterior	latissimus dorsi	subscapularis
external intercostals	internal intercostals	rhomboideus major	rhomboideus minor
levator scapulae	supraspinatus	infraspinatus	teres major
teres minor			

Upper appendage

biceps brachii	triceps brachii	brachialis	brachioradialis
pronator teres	palmaris longus	supinator	flexor carpi ulnaris
flexor carpi radialis	extensor carpi radialis longus	extensor carpi ulnaris	flexor digitorum profundus
extensor carpi radialis brevis	flexor digitorum superficialis	flexor pollicis longus	extensor digitorum

Abdomen

external oblique	internal oblique	rectus abdominus	transverse abdominus

Lower appendage

gluteus maximus	gluteus medius	gluteus minimus	adductor longus
adductor brevis	adductor magnus	biceps femoris	semimembranosus
semitendinosus	rectus femoris	vastus lateralis	vastus medialis
vastus intermedius	tensor fascia latae	tibialis posterior	tibialis anterior
sartorius	gracilis	gastrocnemius	soleus
pectineus	psoas major	iliacus	extensor hallicis longus
extensor digitorum longus	flexor digitorum longus	fibularis (peroneus) longus	fibularis (peroneus) brevis

Tips:

1. Identifying and learning the function of these muscles will be easy if the criteria used to name skeletal muscles is known. Following are some of the common ones.

    a) Muscles are named according to the *direction of the muscle fibers*. For example, transverse abdominus, internal and external oblique run at right angles and obliquely with reference to the long axis of the body

    b) Muscles are named according to the *size of the muscle*. Gluteus maximus (large), gluteus minimus (small), radialis longus (long)

    c) Muscles are named based on *the number of origins*. When the muscle has two or three or four origins (heads) they are known as biceps (bi=two), triceps (tri=three), quadriceps (quad=four),respectively

    d) Muscles are named based on their *locations*. For example: frontalis is over the frontal bone, occipitalis is over the occipital bone

    e) Muscles are named based on their *shape*. For example the trapezius muscle resembles a trapezoid, deltoid muscle is triangular, pectinate is comb-shaped

f) Muscles are named based on the location of their *origin and insertion*. Sternocleidomastoid has its origin on the sternum and clavicle (cleido) and inserts into the mastoid process of the temporal bone

g) Muscles are named based on their *action*. For example flexors bring about flexion, extensors bring about extension, abductors bring about abduction etc.

2. The origin of a muscle is the nonmoving attachment and the insertion is the moving attachment.

3. Concentrate on the information the name provides. This will provide information as to the location of the muscle.

4. Try to relate the muscle's location, origin and insertion to its actions. Try to enact the action of individual muscle.

Checklist:

A. Muscular tissues

_____ cardiac muscle tissue   _____ striations (A and I bands)

_____ skeletal muscle tissue   _____ sarcolemma

_____ smooth muscle tissue   _____ sarcoplasmic reticulum

_____ intercalated discs   _____ sarcomere

B. Connective tissue sheaths

_____ endomysium   _____ epimysium

_____ perimysium   _____ fascicle

C. Neuromuscular junction

_____ axonal terminals   _____ motor neuron axon

_____ muscle cell

D. Identification of skeletal muscles

_____ muscles of the head   _____ muscles of the deep neck

_____ muscles of the anterior thorax   _____ muscles of the posterior thorax

_____ muscles of upper appendage   _____ muscles of lower appendage

_____ Abdominal muscles

_____ origin, insertion, action and nerve supply of each muscle

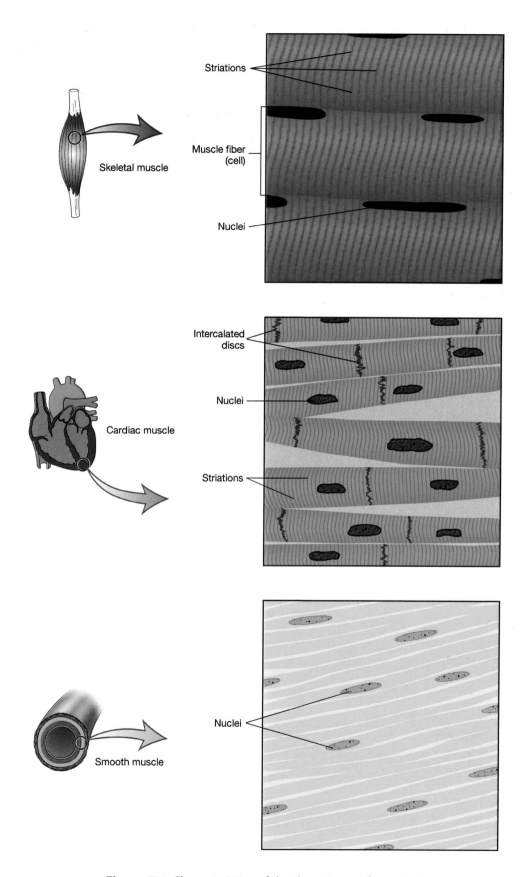

Figure 7.1: Characteristics of the three types of muscle tissue

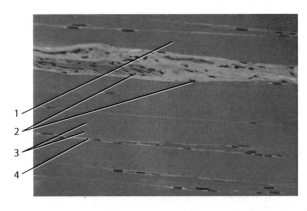

Figure 7.2: Skeletal muscle. 1) Skeletal muscle cell 2) Nuclei 3) Striations 4) Connective tissue

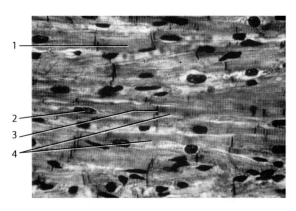

Figure 7.3: Cardiac muscle. 1) Cardiac muscle cell 2) Nucleus 3) Intercalated disc 4) Striations

Figure 7.4: Neuromuscular junction. 1) Muscle fibers 2) Axon terminals 3) Motor neuron axon

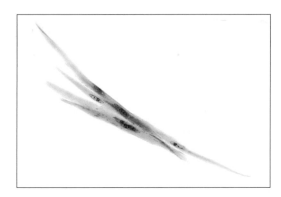

Figure 7.5: Smooth muscle tissue, teased

© bluedoor, LLC

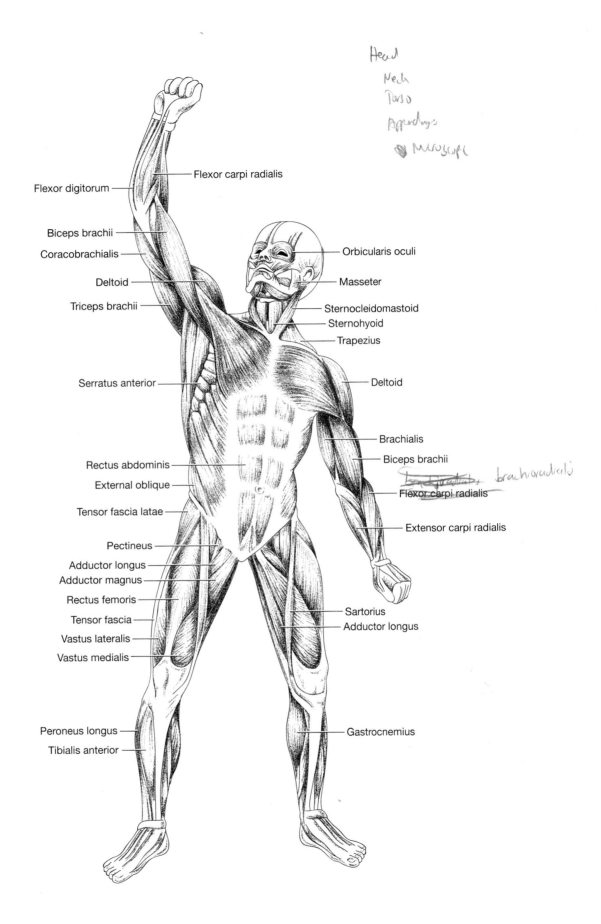

Flexor carpi radialis
Flexor digitorum
Biceps brachii
Coracobrachialis
Deltoid
Triceps brachii
Serratus anterior
Rectus abdominis
External oblique
Tensor fascia latae
Pectineus
Adductor longus
Adductor magnus
Rectus femoris
Tensor fascia
Vastus lateralis
Vastus medialis
Peroneus longus
Tibialis anterior

Orbicularis oculi
Masseter
Sternocleidomastoid
Sternohyoid
Trapezius
Deltoid
Brachialis
Biceps brachii
Flexor carpi radialis
Extensor carpi radialis
Sartorius
Adductor longus
Gastrocnemius

brachioradialis

Head
Neck
Torso
Appendages
Microscope

Figure 7.6: Muscular sytem, anterior view.

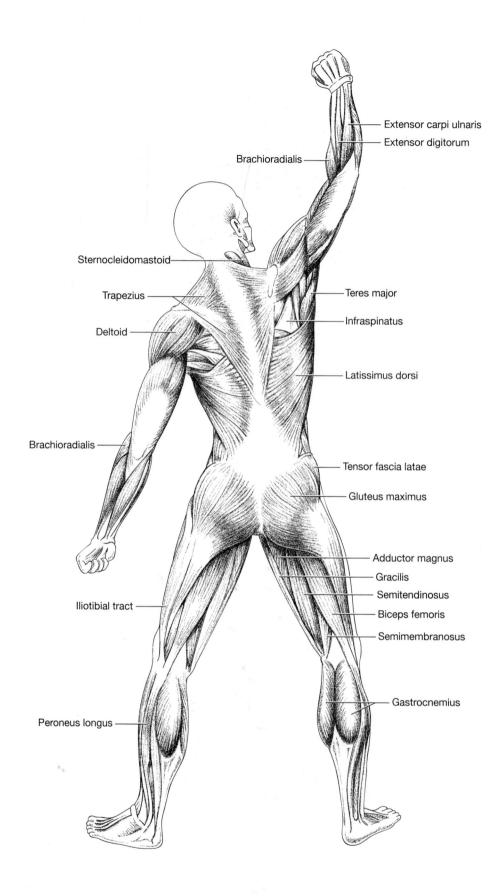

Extensor carpi ulnaris

Extensor digitorum

Brachioradialis

Sternocleidomastoid

Trapezius

Deltoid

Teres major

Infraspinatus

Latissimus dorsi

Brachioradialis

Tensor fascia latae

Gluteus maximus

Adductor magnus

Gracilis

Semitendinosus

Biceps femoris

Semimembranosus

Iliotibial tract

Gastrocnemius

Peroneus longus

Figure 7.7: Muscular sytem, posterior view.

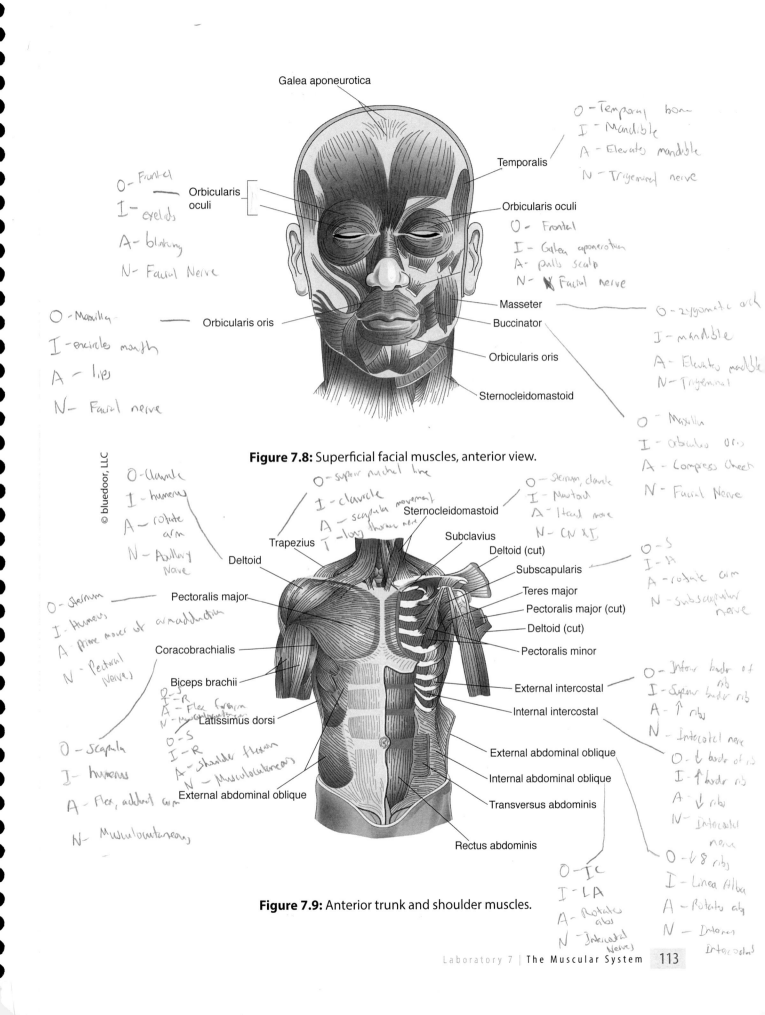

Figure 7.8: Superficial facial muscles, anterior view.

Galea aponeurotica

Temporalis

O - Temporal bone
I - Mandible
A - Elevates mandible
N - Trigeminal nerve

O - Frontal
I - eyelids
A - blinking
N - Facial Nerve

Orbicularis oculi

Orbicularis oculi

O - Frontal
I - Galea aponeurotica
A - pulls scalp
N - Facial nerve

O - Maxilla
I - encircles mouth
A - lips
N - Facial nerve

Orbicularis oris

Masseter

Buccinator

O - zygomatic arch
I - mandible
A - Elevates mandible
N - Trigeminal

Orbicularis oris

Sternocleidomastoid

O - Maxilla
I - orbicularis oris
A - Compress cheek
N - Facial Nerve

© bluedoor, LLC

O - Clavicle
I - humerus
A - rotate arm
N - Axillary Nerve

O - superior nuchal line
I - clavicle
A - scapula movement
N - long thoracic nerve

Trapezius

Sternocleidomastoid

O - Sternum, clavicle
I - Mastoid
A - Head move
N - CN XI

Deltoid

Subclavius

Deltoid (cut)

Subscapularis

O - Sternum
I - Humerus
A - Prime mover of arm adduction
N - Pectoral Nerves

Pectoralis major

Teres major

Pectoralis major (cut)

Deltoid (cut)

Pectoralis minor

O - S
I - H
A - rotate arm
N - Subscapular nerve

Coracobrachialis

O - S
I - R
A - Flex forearm
N - Musculocutaneous

Biceps brachii

External intercostal

Internal intercostal

O - Inferior border of rib
I - Superior border rib
A - ↑ ribs
N - Intercostal nerve

O - Scapula
I - humerus
A - Flex, adduct arm
N - Musculocutaneous

O - S
I - R
A - shoulder flexion
N - Musculocutaneous

Latissimus dorsi

External abdominal oblique

External abdominal oblique

Internal abdominal oblique

Transversus abdominis

O - t border of rib
I - ↑ border rib
A - ↓ ribs
N - Intercostal nerve

Rectus abdominis

O - IC
I - LA
A - Rotate abs
N - Intercostal Nerves

O - ↓ 8 ribs
I - Linea Alba
A - Rotate abs
N - Internal Intercostal

Figure 7.9: Anterior trunk and shoulder muscles.

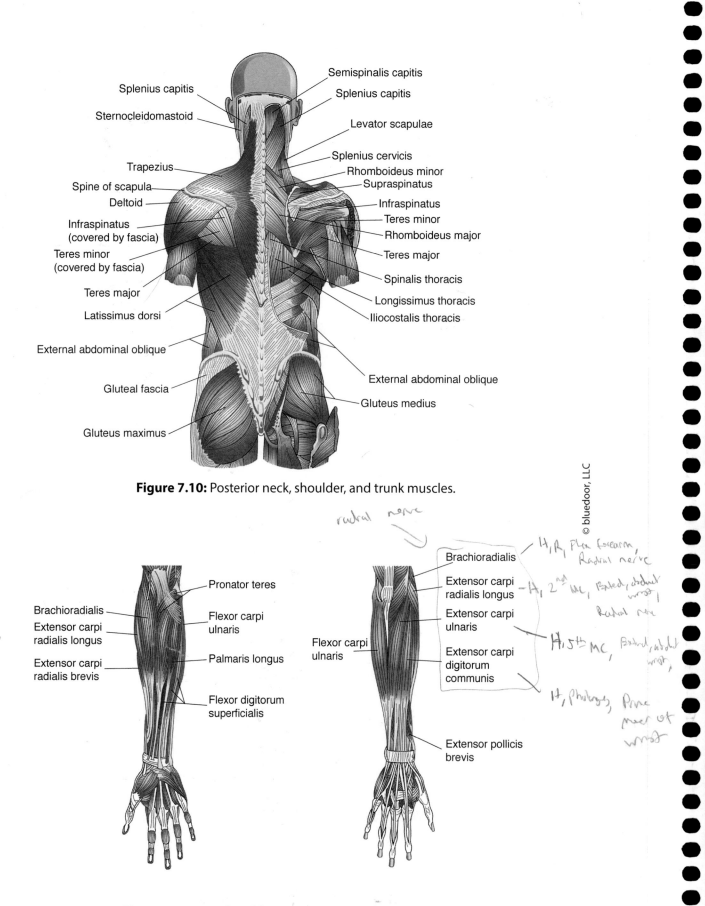

Figure 7.10: Posterior neck, shoulder, and trunk muscles.

Splenius capitis
Semispinalis capitis
Splenius capitis
Sternocleidomastoid
Levator scapulae
Splenius cervicis
Trapezius
Rhomboideus minor
Spine of scapula
Supraspinatus
Deltoid
Infraspinatus
Infraspinatus (covered by fascia)
Teres minor
Rhomboideus major
Teres minor (covered by fascia)
Teres major
Teres major
Spinalis thoracis
Latissimus dorsi
Longissimus thoracis
Iliocostalis thoracis
External abdominal oblique
External abdominal oblique
Gluteal fascia
Gluteus medius
Gluteus maximus

radial nerve

Brachioradialis
Pronator teres
Brachioradialis
Extensor carpi radialis longus
Extensor carpi radialis longus
Flexor carpi ulnaris
Extensor carpi ulnaris
Extensor carpi radialis brevis
Palmaris longus
Flexor carpi ulnaris
Extensor carpi digitorum communis
Flexor digitorum superficialis
Extensor pollicis brevis

Figure 7.11: Muscles of forearm, anterior and posterior views.

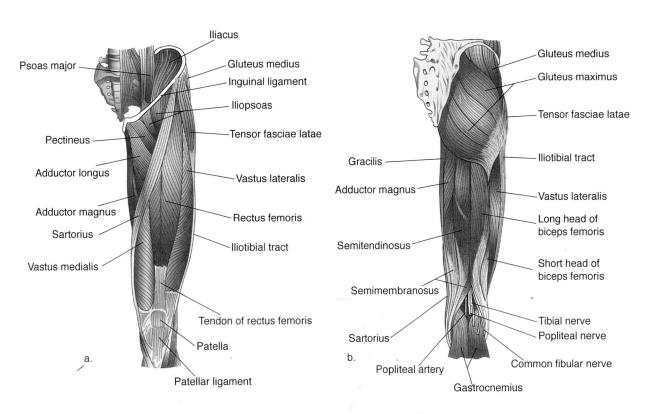

Figure 7.12: a. anterior thigh muscles, b. posterior thigh muscles

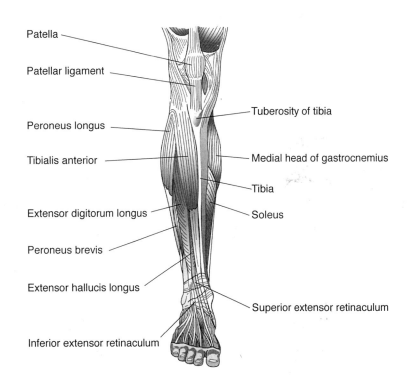

Figure 7.13: Anterior lower leg muscles

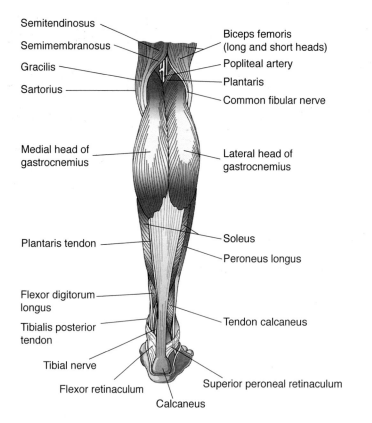

Semitendinosus

Semimembranosus

Gracilis

Sartorius

Biceps femoris
(long and short heads)

Popliteal artery

Plantaris

Common fibular nerve

Medial head of
gastrocnemius

Lateral head of
gastrocnemius

Plantaris tendon

Soleus

Peroneus longus

Flexor digitorum
longus

Tibialis posterior
tendon

Tendon calcaneus

Tibial nerve

Flexor retinaculum

Superior peroneal retinaculum

Calcaneus

© bluedoor, LLC

Figure 7.14: Posterior lower leg muscles

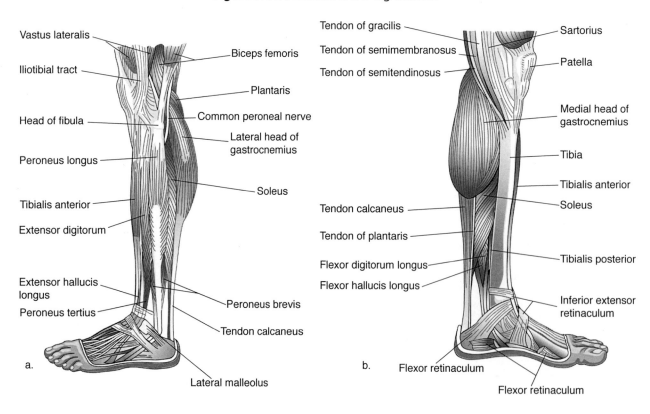

Vastus lateralis

Iliotibial tract

Head of fibula

Peroneus longus

Tibialis anterior

Extensor digitorum

Extensor hallucis
longus

Peroneus tertius

Biceps femoris

Plantaris

Common peroneal nerve

Lateral head of
gastrocnemius

Soleus

Peroneus brevis

Tendon calcaneus

a.

Lateral malleolus

Tendon of gracilis

Tendon of semimembranosus

Tendon of semitendinosus

Sartorius

Patella

Medial head of
gastrocnemius

Tibia

Tibialis anterior

Soleus

Tendon calcaneus

Tendon of plantaris

Flexor digitorum longus

Flexor hallucis longus

Tibialis posterior

Inferior extensor
retinaculum

b.

Flexor retinaculum

Flexor retinaculum

Figure 7.15: a. Lateral lower leg muscles, b. Medial lower leg muscles.

Name: _____

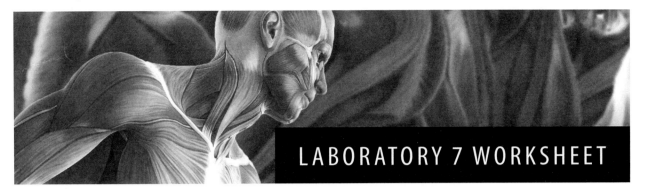

LAB 7 WORKSHEET

1. Prepare labeled drawings as seen under the microscope.

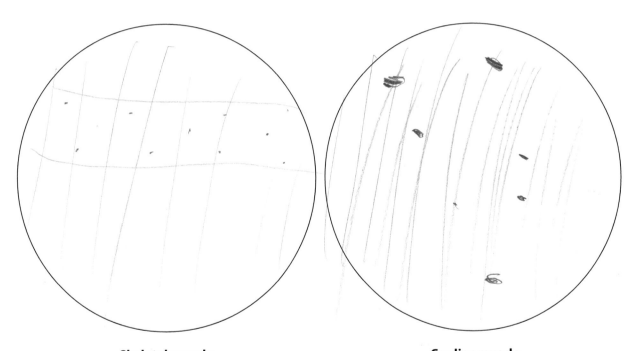

Skeletal muscle

Total magnification: _____
Label the nucleus, A band, I band
sarcolemma, sarcomere

Cardiac muscle

Total magnification: _____
Label the nucleus, intercalated disc
sarcolemma

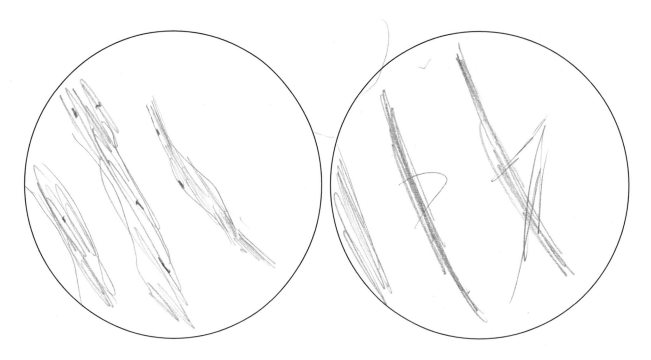

Smooth muscle

Total magnification: _____
Label the nucleus, sarcolemma

Neuromuscular junction

Total magnification: _____
Label the axon, axonal terminal
muscle fiber

1. Identify the muscles that perform each function

Name three flexors of the shoulder

~~Pectoral~~ ~~minor~~ Biceps

Trapezius   Deltoid

Rhomboideus   Pectoralis major

Prime movers of shoulder adduction

Pectoralis minor

Levator scapulae

Prime mover of shoulder abduction

Deltoid

Two **prime movers** of shoulder extension

Deltoid

Teres minor

Used when shrugging the shoulders

Trapezius

Two **prime movers** of elbow flexion

biceps brachii

~~triceps brachii~~ Brachioradialis

Prime mover of elbow extension

Triceps brachii

Prime mover of forearm pronation

Pronator teres

Two muscles of forearm supination

biceps brachii

brachioradialis

Two **prime movers** of wrist flexion

flexor carpi radialis

flexor carpi ulnaris

Prime mover of wrist extension

Extensor carpi radialis longus

Two abductors of the wrist

Flexor carpi radialis

Extensor carpi radialis longus

Prime mover of inspiration

Respiratory ~~diaphragm~~ diaphragm

Two muscles that close the jaw

masseter

temporalis

Flexes and laterally rotates the head

Sternocleidomastoid

Prime mover of jaw closure

masseter

Prime mover of hip flexion

Iliopsoas

Two **prime movers** of hip extension

gluteus maximus

gluteus minimus

Three **prime movers** of knee flexion _____ ~~sartor~~ bicep femors_____

_____ Semimembranous_____

_____ semitendinous_____

Two **prime movers** of knee extension _____ Rectus femors_____

_____ Vastus ~~~~ medalis_____

Prime mover of dorsiflexion _____ tibralis anterior_____

Two **prime movers** of plantar flexion _____ gastrocnemius_____

_____ soleus_____

Prime mover of ankle inversion _____ tibralis anterior_____

Two muscles of ankle eversion _____ fibularis longus_____

_____ fibularis brevis_____

Action of the hamstrings at the hip _____ ~~adduct~~ extension_____

Action of the hamstrings at the knee _____ flexion_____

POST LAB WORKSHEET LAB 7

1. Match the terms with the appropriate statement

   Sarcolemma   sarcoplasm   sarcomere   intercalated discs

   A bands   I bands

   Junctions found only in cardiac muscle   _____ _____

   Contractile unit of a muscle   _____

   The dark bands of the sarcomere   _____

   The light bands of the sarcomere   _____

   Plasma membrane of a muscle cell   _____

   Cytoplasm of a muscle cell   _____

2. Label the following diagram using the following terms:

   Muscle fiber   perimysium   fascicle   endomysium   epimysium

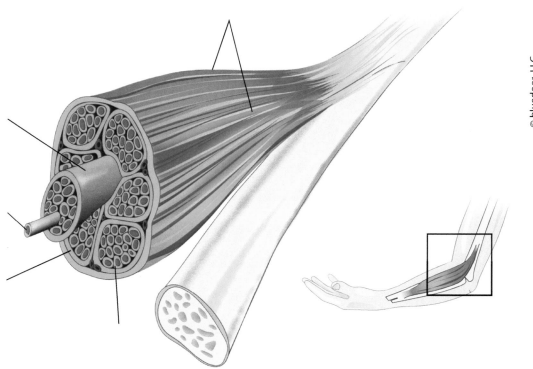

© bluedoor, LLC

MUSCLE TABLES

Muscles of Facial Expression • All are innervated by the facial nerve (CN VII)				
Muscle	**Origin**	**Insertion**	**Action**	**Innervation**
Frontalis	Galea aponeurotica	Skin of eyebrows and root of nose	Raises eyebrows; wrinkles forehead	Facial nerve (CN VII)
Occipitalis	Occipital and temporal bone	Galea aponeurotica	Pulls scalp posterioly	Facial nerve (CN VII)
Orbicularis oculi	Frontal and maxillary bones	Tissue of the eyelid	Produces blinking, squinting, and draws eyebrows inferiorly	Facial nerve (CN VII)
Buccinator	Maxilla and mandible	Orbicularis oris	Compresses the cheek (as in whistling)	Facial nerve (CN VII)
Orbicularis oris	Arises indirectly from the maxilla and mandible	Encircles the mouth, inserts onto skin and muscles at lateral corners of mouth	Closes the lips; purses and protrudes the lips, as in whistling and kissing	Facial nerve (CN VII)
Mentalis	Mandible	Skin of the chin	Protrudes lower lip; wrinkles the chin	Facial nerve (CN VII)

Muscles of Mastication (Chewing)
• All are innervated by the trigeminal nerve (CN V)

Muscle	Origin	Insertion	Action	Innervation
Masseter	Zygomatic arch	Mandible	Elevates mandible	Trigeminal nerve (CN V)
Temporalis	Occipital and temporal bone	Mandible	Elevates mandible	Trigeminal nerve (CN V)

Muscles of the Neck and Back
• All are innervated by spinal nerves except sternocleidomastoid

Muscle	Origin	Insertion	Action	Innervation
Splenius	Vertebrae C_7-T_6	Temporal and occipital bone	Acting together extend the head; acting alone head is rotated and bent toward the same side	Spinal nerves
Sternocleidomastoid	Sternum and clavicle	Mastoid process of the temporal bone	Acting together flex the head; acting alone rotates head toward the opposite shoulder	Accessory nerve (CN XI)
Semispinalis	Vertebrae C_7-T_{12}	Occipital bone and cervical and thoracic vertebrae (to T_4)	Extends vertebral column and head, rotates to opposite side	Spinal nerves

Erector spinae group – prime movers of back extension, arranged as three vertically running columns from medial to lateral:

Muscle	Origin	Insertion	Action	Innervation
Spinalis (most medial)	Upper lumbar to lower thoracic vertebrae	Upper thoracic to cervical vertebrae	Extends vertebral column	Spinal nerves
Longissimus (intermediate)	Lumbar through cervical vertebrae	Thoracic through cervical vertebrae and rib	Extend and laterally flex vertebral column	

| \multicolumn{5}{c}{**Muscles of the Thorax Relating to Respiratory Movements**
• All are innervated by intercostal nerves except the respiratory diaphragm} |
Muscle	**Origin**	**Insertion**	**Action**	**Innervation**
External intercostals	Inferior border of the rib above	Superior border of the rib below	Elevates rib cage, assists in forced inspiration	Intercostal nerves
Internal intercostals	Superior border of the rib below	Inferior border of the rib above	Depress the rib cage, assists in forced expiration	Intercostal nerves
Respiratory diaphragm	Rib cage, sternum, and lumbar vertebrae	Central tendon	Prime mover of inspiration	Phrenic nerve

Muscles of the Thorax Relating to Movements of the Scapula

Muscle	Origin	Insertion	Action	Innervation
Pectoralis minor	Ribs 3-5	Scapula	Stabilizes scapula by drawing it forward and down ward	Pectoral nerves
Serratus anterior	Ribs 1-8	Scapula	Protracts and holds scapula against the thoracic wall	Long thoracic nerve
Trapezius	Superior nuchal line, ligamentum nuchae, and vertebrae C_7 through T_{12}	Clavicle, scapula	Elevates, retracts, and rotates scapula	Accessory nerve (CN XI)
Levator scapulae	Vertebrae C_1 through C_4	Scapula	Elevates the scapula	Cervical spinal nerves and dorsal scapular nerve
Rhomboids	Vertebrae C_7 through T_5	Scapula	Retracts and stabilizes scapula	Dorsal scapular nerve

	Muscles Acting on the Arm Anterior Group			
Muscle	Origin	Insertion	Action	Innervation
Pectoralis major	Sternum, costal cartilages, and clavicle	Humerus	Flexes, adducts, and medially rotates arm	Pectoral nerves
Deltoid (anterior fibers)	Clavicle (scapula for lateral and posterior fibers)	Deltoid tuberosity of the humerus	Flexes, extends, abducts, and medially rotates arm	Axillary nerve
Coracobrachialis	Scapula	Humerus	Flexes and adducts arm	Musculocutaneous
Biceps brachii Long head Short head	Scapula	Radius	Weak shoulder flexion (also flexes the elbow and supinates forearm)	Musculocutaneous

Prime mover of arm adductor (handwritten annotation)

	Muscles Acting on the Arm Posterior Group			
Muscle	**Origin**	**Insertion**	**Action**	**Innervation**
Deltoid (lateral and posterior part)	Scapula	Humerus	Flexes, extends, abducts, and laterally rotates arm	Axillary nerve
Supraspinatus*	Scapula	Greater tubercle of the humerus	Assists in arm abduction, stabilizes shoulder joint	Suprascapular nerve
Infraspinatus*	Scapula	Greater tubercle of the humerus	Laterally rotates arm, stabilizes shoulder joint	Suprascapular nerve
Teres minor*	Scapula	Greater tubercle of the humerus	Laterally rotates arm, stabilizes shoulder joint	Axillary nerve
Subscapularis*	Scapula	Lesser tubercle of the humerus	Medially rotates arm, stabilizes shoulder joint	Subscapular nerve
Teres major	Scapula	Humerus	Extends, adducts, and medially rotates arm	Subscapular nerve
Triceps brachii long head	Scapula	Ulna	Extends and assists in arm adduction	Radial nerve
Latissimuss Dorsi	Thoracic and lumbar vertebrae, ribs, iliac crest	Humerus	Extends, adducts and medially rotates arm	Thoracodorsal nerve

*SITS = muscles of the rotator cuff, major stabilizer of the shoulder joint

Muscles Acting on the Forearm
Anterior *flexor* compartment

Muscle	Origin	Insertion	Action	Innervation
Biceps brachii	Scapula	Radius	Flex and supinate forearm	Musculocutaneous nerve
Brachialis	Humerus	Ulna	Flex forearm	
Pronator Teres	Humerus and proximal ulna	Midradius	Pronates forearm	Median nerve
Brachioradialis	Humerus	Radius	Flexes forearm	Radial nerve

Muscles Acting on the Forearm
Posterior *extensor* compartment
• All are innervated by the radial nerve

Muscle		Origin	Insertion	Action	Innervation
Triceps brachii					
	Long head	Scapula	Ulna	Extends forearm at elbow	Radial nerve
	Lateral head	Humerus			
	Medial head	Humerus			
Supinator		Humerus and ulna	Midradius	Supinates forearm	

Muscles Acting on the Wrist and Hand Anterior *flexor* compartment				
Muscle	**Origin**	**Insertion**	**Action**	**Innervation**
Palmaris longus	Medial epicondyle of the humerus	Palmar aponeurosis	Flex wrist	Median nerve
Flexor carpi ulnaris	Medial epicondyle of the humerus and ulna	Fifth metacarpal and pisiform and hammate	Flex wrist, adducts hand	Ulnar nerve
Flexor carpi radialis	Medial epicondyle of the humerus	Second and third metacarpal	Flex wrist, abducts hand	Median nerve
Flexor digitorum superficialis	Medial epicondyle of the humerus, ulna, and radius	Phalanges of fingers 2-5	Flexes wrist and middle phlanges of fingers 2-5	Median nerve
Flexor digitorum profundus	Ulna	Phalanges of fingers 2-5	Flexes distal and proximal interphalangeqal joint, metacarpophalangeal joint, and wrist	Median (lateral half) and ulnar (medial half) nerves
Flexor pollicis longus	Radius	Thumb	Flexes distal phalanx of the thumb	Median nerve

Muscles Acting on the Wrist and hand Posterior *extensor* compartment • All are innervated by the radial nerve				
Muscle	**Origin**	**Insertion**	**Action**	**Innervation**
Extensor carpi radialis longus	Lateral epicondyle of the humerus	Second metacarpal	Extends and abducts wrist	Radial nerve
Extensor carpi radialis brevis		Third metacarpal	Extends and abducts wrist	
Extensor carpi ulnaris		Fifth metacarpal	Extends and adducts wrist	
Extensor digitorum		Phalanges of fingers 2-5	Prime mover of finger extension, extends wrist	

Muscles of the Anterior and Lateral Abdominal Wall • All are innervated by intercostal nerves				
Muscle	**Origin**	**Insertion**	**Action**	**Innervation**
External abdominal oblique	Lower 8 ribs	Linea alba	Rotates vertebral column and compresses abdominal contents	Intercostal nerves
Internal abdominal oblique	Iliac crest	Linea alba	Rotates vertebral column and compresses abdominal contents	
Rectus abdominus	Pubis	Xiphoid process and ribs	Flexes vertebral column and compresses abdominal contents	
Transversus abdominus	Last 6 ribs and iliac crest	Linea alba	Compresses abdominal contents	

Hip Flexors Anterior compartment • All are innervated by the femoral nerve				
Muscle	**Origin**	**Insertion**	**Action**	**Innervation**
Iliacus	Ilium	Femur	Flexes thigh	Femoral nerve
Psoas	Lumbar vertebrae	Femur	Flexes thigh	
Rectus femoris	Ilium	Tibia	Flexes thigh (and extends knee)	
Sartorius	Ilium	Tibia	Flexes, abducts, and laterally rotates the thigh ("tailor's muscle")	
Pectineus	Pubis	Femur	Flexes, adducts and medially rotates thigh	

Hip Extensors Posterior compartment • All are innervated by the sciatic nerve (except for gluteus maximus) • Have an origin on the ischial tuberosity (except for the gluteus maximus) Semimembranosus, semitendinosus, and biceps femoris are collectively known as the hamstrings				
Muscle	**Origin**	**Insertion**	**Action**	**Innervation**
Gluteus maximus	Ilium and sacrum	Gluteal tuberosity of the femur	Extends, abducts and laterally rotates thigh	Inferior gluteal nerve
Semitendinosus	Ischial tuberosity	Tibia	Extends thigh; flexes knee	Sciatic nerve
Semimembranosus		Tibia		
Biceps femoris		Fibula		

Hip Adductors
Medial compartment
• All are innervated by the obturator nerve (except for the pectinius)
• Have an origin on the ishium and/or pubis
• Insert onto the medial aspect of the femur (except for the gracilis)

Muscle	Origin	Insertion	Action	Innervation
Adductor magnus	Ischiopubic ramus	Femur	Adducts, flexes, and medially rotates thigh	Obturator nerve
Adductor longus	Pubis	Femur	Adducts, flexes, and medially rotates thigh	
Adductor brevis	Pubis	Femur	Adducts, flexes, and medially rotates thigh	
Pectineus	Pubis	Femur	Adducts, flexes, and medially rotates thigh	Femoral nerve
Gracilis	Ischiopubic ramus	Tibia	Adducts, flexes, and medially rotates thigh; flexes knee	Obturator nerve

Hip Abductors
Lateral compartment
• All are innervated by the superior gluteal nerve
• Have an origin on the ilium
• Insert onto the greater trochanter of the femur (except for the tensor fasciae latae)

Muscle	Origin	Insertion	Action	Innervation
Gluteus medius	Ilium	Femur	Abducts and aids in medial rotation of the thigh	Superior gluteal nerve
Gluteus minimus		Femur		
Tensor fasciae latae		Iliotibial tract	Abducts, flexes, and aids in medial rotation of the thigh	

Extensors of the Knee
Anterior compartment
• All are innervated by the femoral nerve
• Insert onto the tibial tuberosity
• All four muscles are collectively known as the the quadriceps femoris

Muscle	Origin	Insertion	Action	Innervation
Rectus femoris*	Ilium	Tibial tuberosity	Extends knee (rectus femoris also flexes thigh)	Femoral nerve
Vastus lateralis	Proximal femur			
Vastus intermedius				
Vastus medialis				

Flexors of the Knee				
Posterior compartment				
• All are innervated by the sciatic nerve (except for gracilis)				
• Have an origin on the ischial tuberosity (except for the gracilis)				
Muscle	**Origin**	**Insertion**	**Action**	**Innervation**
Semitendinosus	Ischial tuberosity	Tibia	Flexes knee	Sciatic nerve
Semimembranosus		Tibia		
Biceps femoris		Fibula		
Gracilis	Ischiopubic ramus	Tibia		Obturator nerve

Plantar flexors and inverters of the foot
Posterior compartment
• All are innervated by the tibial nerve

Muscle	Origin	Insertion	Action	Innervation
Gastrocnemius	Femur	Calcaneous	Plantar flexes foot (and can flex knee when foot is dorsiflexed)	Tibial nerve
Soleus	Tibia and Fibula	Calcaneous	Plantar flexes foot	
Tibialis posterior	Tibia and Fibula	Medial cuniform and navicular	Plantar flexes and inverts foot	
Flexor digitorum longus	Tibia	Phalanges of toes 2-5	Plantar flexes and inverts foot, flexes toes	

Plantar Flexors And Everters of the Foot
Lateral compartment
• All are innervated by the superficial fibular nerve

Muscle	Origin	Insertion	Action	Innervation
Fibularis (peroneus) longus	fibula	Fifth metatarsal	Plantar flexes and everts foot	Superficial fibular (peroneal) nerve
Fibularis (peroneus) brevis				

Dorsiflexors of the foot Anterior compartment • All are innervated by the deep fibular (peroneal nerve)				
Muscle	**Origin**	**Insertion**	**Action**	**Innervation**
Tibialis anterior	Tibia	Medial cuniform and dorsal surface first metatarsal	Dorsiflexes and inverts foot	Deep fibular (peroneal) nerve
Extensor digitorum longus	Tibia and fibula	Middle and distal phalanges of toes 2-5	Toe extension, dorsiflexes foot	
Extensor hallucis longus	Fibula	Distal phalanx of great toe	Extends great toe, dorsiflexes foot	

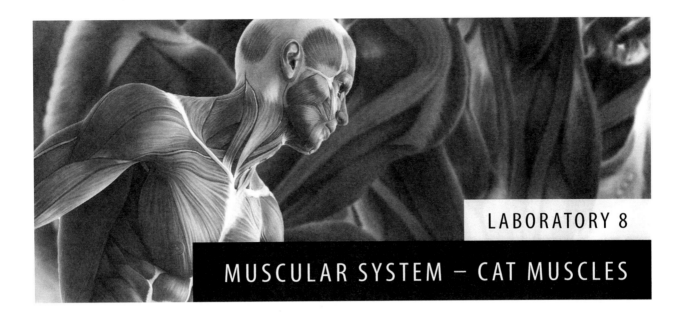

MUSCULAR SYSTEM – CAT MUSCLES

Objectives

Identify the following skeletal muscles of the cat:

Neck muscles

sternomastoid	cleidomastoid

Abdominal muscles

External oblique	Internal oblique	Rectus abdominus

Shoulder/thorax muscles

pectoralis major	pectoralis minor	xiphihumeralis	pectoantebrachialis
clavotrapezius	acromiotrapezius	spinotrapezius	latissimus dorsi
acromiodeltoid	spinodeltoid	clavodeltoid	subscapularis
infraspinatus	supraspinatus	serratus ventralis	splenius
levator scapuli ventralis			

Forelimb

biceps brachii	triceps brachii	brachialis	palmaris longus
flexor carpi ulnaris	flexor carpi radialis	extensor carpi radialis brevis	extensor carpi radialis longus
brachioradialis	extensor carpi ulnaris		

Hindlimb

sartorius	gracilis	adductor longus	Adductor femoris
semimembranosus	semitendinosus	biceps femoris	tensor fascia latae
rectus femoris	vastus intermedius	vastus medialis	gluteus medius
gluteus maximus	caudofemoralis	gastrocnemius	soleus
tibialis anterior			

INTRODUCTION

In the previous lab exercise, identification of human skeletal muscles was done through charts and models. In this lab exercise you will dissect a preserved specimen of a cat and identify the major muscles. Most of the skeletal muscles in mammals are named in a similar fashion. Some muscles that are present in animals are lacking in humans and some muscles that are separate may be fused in humans. This lab activity will help to familiarize the major muscles.

Materials

1. Each group of students should have:

    Dissection tray

    Preserved cat

    Dissection tools: scalpel, blunt probe, pointed probe, scissors, forceps, twine, disposable gloves

2. Materials to be shared by students:

    Cat dissection manuals

ACTIVITY 1

Cat muscle Identification

Resources: Photographic atlas pages 170 -176
Pictorial anatomy of the cat pages 16 - 36
(provided in the lab)

Dissect and identify the cat muscles listed below:

Neck muscles

sternomastoid	cleidomastoid

Abdominal muscles

internal oblique	external oblique	rectus abdominus

Shoulder/thorax muscles

pectoralis major	pectoralis minor	xiphihumeralis	pectoantebrachialis
clavotrapezius	acromiotrapezius	spinotrapezius	latissimus dorsi
acromiodeltoid	spinodeltoid	clavodeltoid	subscapularis
infraspinatus	supraspinatus	serratus ventralis	splenius
levator scapuli ventralis			

Forelimb

biceps brachii	triceps brachii	brachialis	palmaris longus
flexor carpi ulnaris	flexor carpi radialis	extensor carpi radialis brevis	extensor carpi radialis longus
brachioradialis	extensor carpi ulnaris		

Hindlimb

sartorius	gracilis	adductor longus	adductor femoris
semimembranosus	semitendinosus	biceps femoris	tensor fascia latae
rectus femoris	vastus intermedius	vastus medialis	gluteus medius
gluteus maximus	caudofemoralis	gastrocnemius	soleus
tibialis anterior			

Tips:

1. The preserved specimens are already embalmed in a solution to prevent the decaying of tissues and to keep the cat from drying out. So do not dispose of this fluid when you remove the cat from the plastic bag. In addition you will have to preserve the cat again for future review.

2. Proper separation of the fascia from the muscles and one muscle from another will ensure easy identification of muscles.

3. When you want to cut through the superficial muscles always cut halfway between its origin and insertion.

4. Look carefully to see the change in direction of the muscle fibers from one muscle to another. Once these lines have been identified, use a blunt probe to slide back and forth to break the fibers and separate the muscles. If the separation lines have been identified correctly then the muscle will appear clean with no tearing. If it appears ragged then the muscle fibers are being torn and complete separation was not done.

5. After completing the dissection and before leaving the lab dispose of any tissue remnants and paper towels in the proper container or bag and wash the dissection tools, tray with soap and disinfectants, rinse and dry.

Check list:

_____ neck muscles

_____ abdominal muscles

_____ shoulder/thorax muscles

_____ forelimb muscles

_____ hind limb muscles

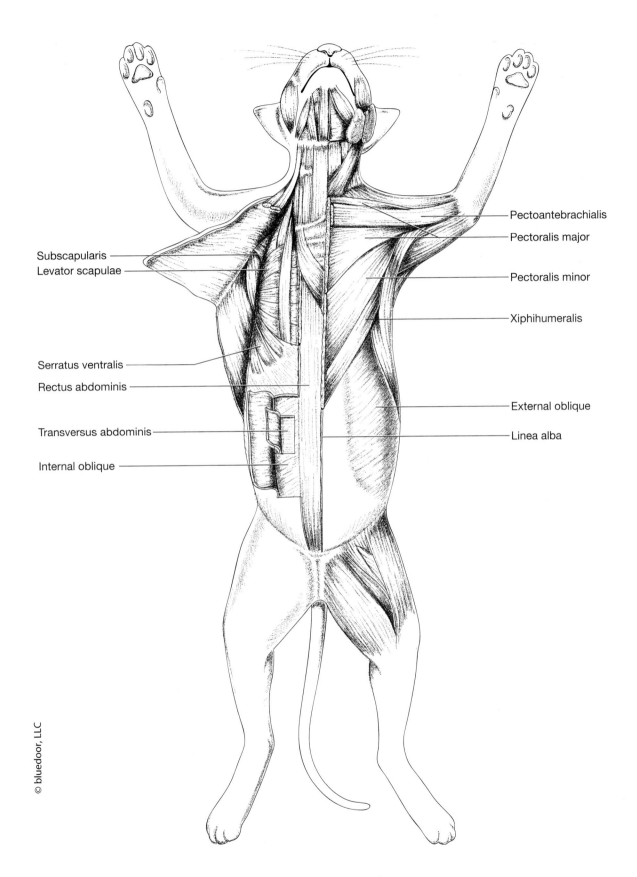

Subscapularis

Levator scapulae

Serratus ventralis

Rectus abdominis

Transversus abdominis

Internal oblique

Pectoantebrachialis

Pectoralis major

Pectoralis minor

Xiphihumeralis

External oblique

Linea alba

Figure 8.1: Ventral muscles, cat

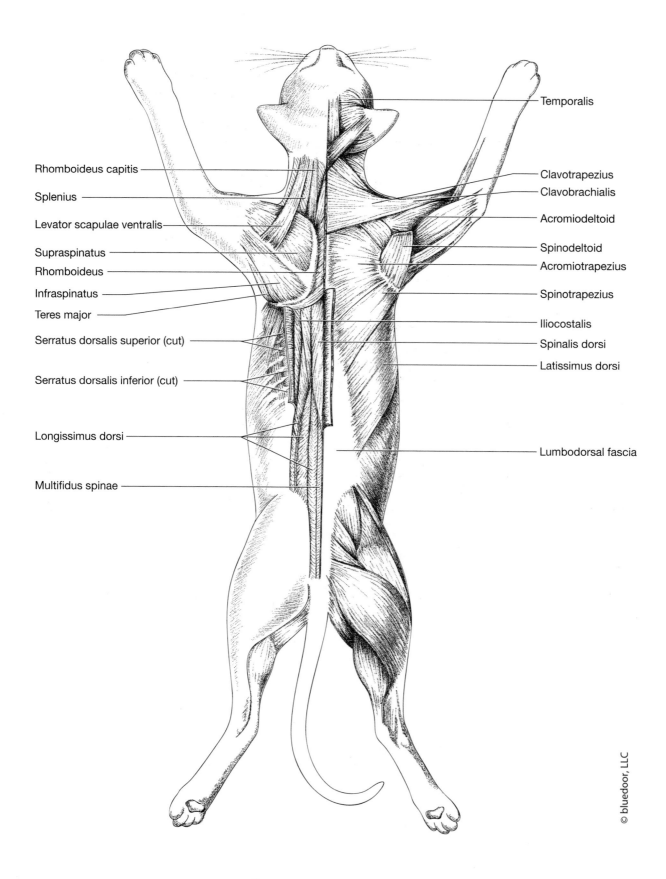

Temporalis

Rhomboideus capitis

Splenius

Levator scapulae ventralis

Supraspinatus

Rhomboideus

Infraspinatus

Teres major

Serratus dorsalis superior (cut)

Serratus dorsalis inferior (cut)

Longissimus dorsi

Multifidus spinae

Clavotrapezius

Clavobrachialis

Acromiodeltoid

Spinodeltoid

Acromiotrapezius

Spinotrapezius

Iliocostalis

Spinalis dorsi

Latissimus dorsi

Lumbodorsal fascia

© bluedoor, LLC

Figure 8.2: Dorsal muscles, cat

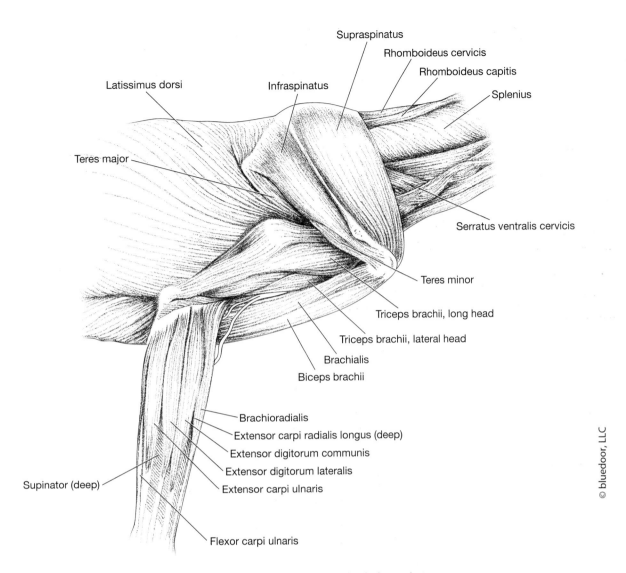

Figure 8.3: Muscles of the forelimb, lateral view, cat

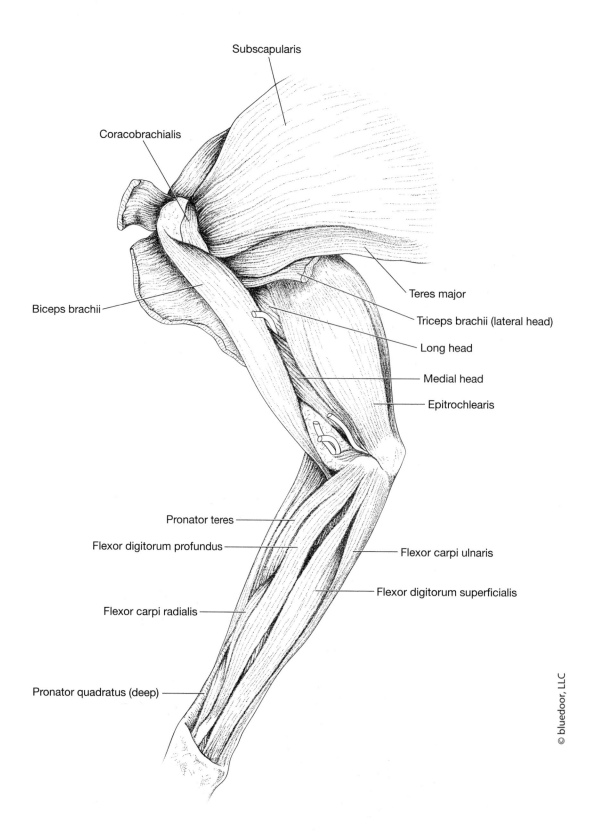

Figure 8.4: Muscles of the forelimb, medial view, cat

- Subscapularis
- Coracobrachialis
- Biceps brachii
- Teres major
- Triceps brachii (lateral head)
- Long head
- Medial head
- Epitrochlearis
- Pronator teres
- Flexor digitorum profundus
- Flexor carpi ulnaris
- Flexor digitorum superficialis
- Flexor carpi radialis
- Pronator quadratus (deep)

© bluedoor, LLC

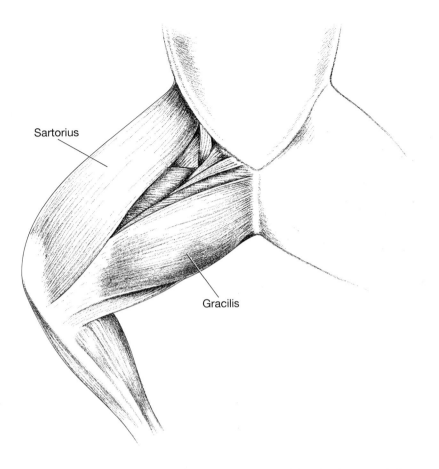

Sartorius

Gracilis

Figure 8.5: Superficial muscles of the thigh, ventral view, cat.

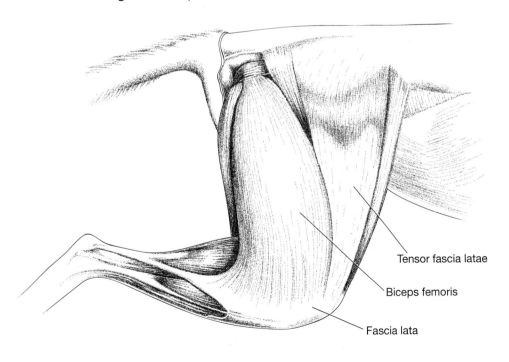

Tensor fascia latae

Biceps femoris

Fascia lata

Figure 8.6: Superficial muscles of the thigh, lateral view, cat

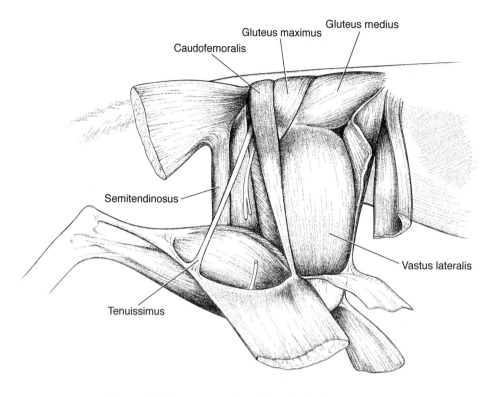

Figure 8.7: Deep muscles of the thigh, lateral view, cat.

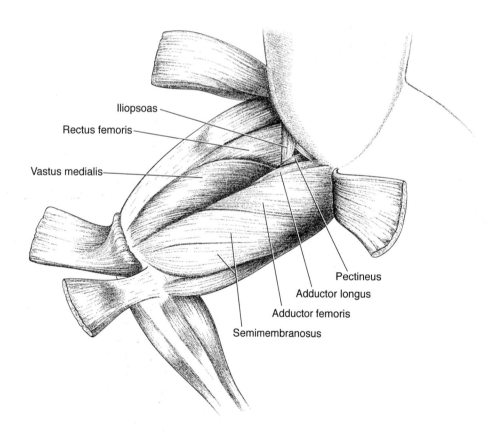

Figure 8.8: Deep muscles of the thigh, ventral view, cat

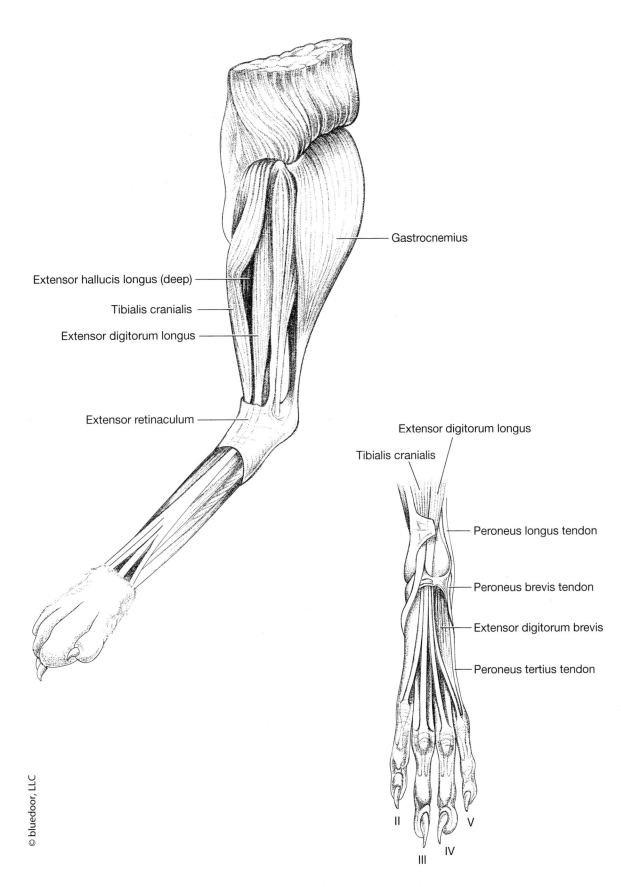

Gastrocnemius

Extensor hallucis longus (deep)

Tibialis cranialis

Extensor digitorum longus

Extensor retinaculum

Extensor digitorum longus

Tibialis cranialis

Peroneus longus tendon

Peroneus brevis tendon

Extensor digitorum brevis

Peroneus tertius tendon

II

III

IV

V

© bluedoor, LLC

Figure 8.9: Muscles of the hindlimb-shank and pes, dorsal view, cat

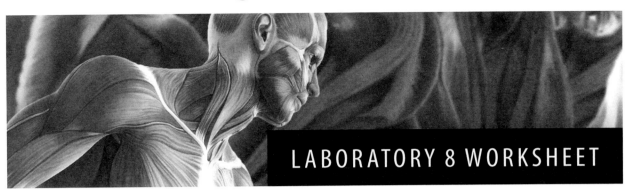

LAB 8 WORKSHEET

Which chest muscle in cats is the largest? *Pectoralis Minor*

Why is the *serratus anterior* in humans called the *serratus ventralis* in cats? *Because the*
serratus is in a different spot because a cat is a quadraped

Which two cat muscles are combined in humans as the *sternocleidomastoid*?
Sternomastoid + Cleidomastoid

The single trapezius muscle in humans comprises which 3 muscles in cats? *Spino trapezius +*
acromiotrapezius + clavotrapezius

Which muscle lies between the *acromiodeltoid* and the *acromiotrapezius*? *Spino deltoid*

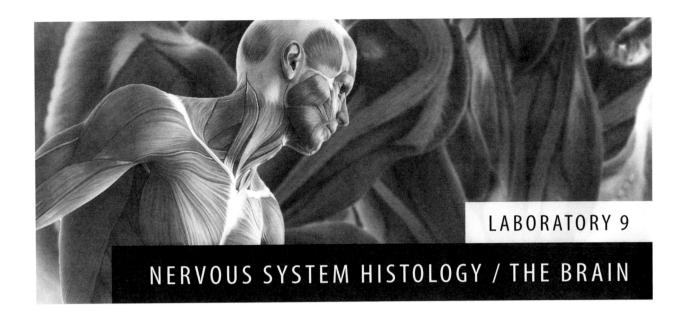

LABORATORY 9

NERVOUS SYSTEM HISTOLOGY / THE BRAIN

Objectives

1. Identify the following portions of a multipolar neuron using a diagram, a model or a prepared slide:

cell body (soma, perikaryon)	Nissl bodies
nucleus	axon hillock
Schwann cell	node of Ranvier
myelin sheath	neurofibril
axon collateral	neurilemma
axon	telodendria (terminal branches)
dendrite	axon terminals (synaptic knobs, boutons)

2. Differentiate between pseudounipolar neurons, bipolar neurons and multipolar neurons using diagrams, models and prepared slides.

3. Identify the following components of a cross-sectioned nerve using diagrams and prepared slides:

   myelin sheath, nerve fibers, fascicles, endoneurium, perineurium and epineurium

4. Identify the following components of the human brain using a diagram or model.

gyrus	fissure	sulcus
longitudinal fissure	central sulcus	frontal lobe

parietal lobe	lateral sulcus	temporal lobe
parieto-occipital sulcus	occipital lobe	postcentral gyrus
cerebellum	pons	medulla oblongata
precentral gyrus	prefrontal cortex	cerebral aqueduct
cerebral white matter	olfactory bulbs	olfactory tracts
optic chiasma	pituitary gland	mammillary bodies
intermediate mass	thalamus	septum pellucidum
fourth ventricle	corpus callosum	fornix
corpora quadrigemina	cerebral cortex	pineal gland
midbrain	superior colliculi	inferior colliculi
interventricular foramen	diencephalon	arbor vitae
dura mater	infundibulum	vermis
arachnoid mater	superior sagittal sinus	hypothalamus
arachnoid villi	subarachnoid space	pia mater
cerebral hemispheres	epithalamus	transverse fissure
lateral ventricle	basal nuclei	choroid plexus
third ventricle	fornix	

5. Identify the following structures of a sheep brain:

longitudinal fissure	corpus callosum	dura mater
corpora quadrigemina	transverse fissure	sulci
gyri	arachnoid mater	pia mater
inferior colliculi	cerebellum	cerebral cortex
epithalamus	superior colliculi	parietal lobe
arbor vitae	olfactory bulbs	optic tract
cerebral hemispheres	olfactory tract	optic chiasma
mammillary body	pituitary gland	infundibulum
medulla oblongata	arbor vitae	central sulcus
meninges	pons	vermis
septum pellucidum	corpus callosum	fornix

intermediate mass	hypothalamus	thalamus
cerebral aqueduct	fourth ventricle	third ventricle
diencephalon	pineal gland	midbrain
lateral ventricle	occipital lobe	frontal lobe
lateral fissure	temporal lobe	

INTRODUCTION

Nervous System Histology

The functional unit of the nervous system is the neuron, a cell that is capable of generating and propagating electrical signals in the form of action potentials. Neurons can be found in the central nervous system (brain and spinal cord) and in the nerves of the peripheral nervous system.

All neurons have three essential components: a cell body (soma), one or more dendrites and a single axon. Neurons can be structurally classified as unipolar (having a single projection from the cell body), bipolar (having two projections from the cell body) or multipolar (having many projections from the cell body).

Neurons are supported structurally and functionally by cells called neuroglia (glial cells). An example of a glial cell is a Schwann cell which produces an insulating myelin sheath for the neurons of the peripheral nervous system.

A nerve is a bundle of axons that is found in the peripheral nervous system. These axons are bundled into fascicles and are supported by a number of connective tissue wrappings. The endoneurium is a delicate layer of loose connective tissue that surrounds individual axons within a fascicle and electrically insulates each axon. The perineurium, a coarser connective tissue wrapping, surrounds the fascicles within the nerve. The entire nerve is surrounded by an epineurium, which is a strong, dense layer of fibrous connective tissue.

THE BRAIN

The brain, located in the cranial cavity, is part of the central nervous system. In this exercise you will learn about the anatomy of the human brain. You will then dissect a sheep brain to identify structures, and to compare it to a human brain.

Materials- Nervous system histology

1. Each student should have a compound microscope.

2. Each pair of students should have:

    Lens paper

    Immersion oil

    Lens cleaner

    Box of prepared slides

    Colored pencils

3. Class materials to be shared by students:

    Three-dimensional models of neurons

    Charts of nervous system histology

ACTIVITY 1:

The Structure of Multipolar Neurons

Resources: Textbook: pages 140, 390 – 393

1. Identify the following components of a multipolar neuron on a three-dimensional model and on diagrams:

cell body (soma, perikaryon)	Nissl bodies
nucleus	axon hillock
Schwann cell	node of Ranvier
myelin sheath	neurofibril
axon collateral	neurilemma
axon	telodendria (terminal branches)
dendrite	axon terminals (synaptic knobs, boutons)

2. Observe a prepared slide of a spinal cord. Select one neuron to study and identify the cell body, nucleus, nucleolus and Nissl bodies. Try to differentiate between the axon and dendrites. Sketch the neuron on the laboratory worksheet.

   Note that the cytoplasm is coarsely textured with dark staining Nissl bodies (rough endoplasmic reticulum). A large nucleus contains a prominent "Owl's eye" nucleolus. A thin axon emerges from the cell body at a conical-shaped axon hillock. Both the axon and axon hillock lack ribosomes and may be recognizable because of their pale-staining cytoplasm. It is also possible that the axon is attached to the top or the bottom of the cell body and is therefore not in your field of view.

3. Observe a prepared slide of myelinated nerve fibers. Identify the nodes of Ranvier, axon (axis cylinder) and myelin sheath. Sketch the nerve fiber on the laboratory worksheet.

ACTIVITY 2:

Structural Classification of Neurons

Resources: Textbook: pages 393-395; 550

1. Observe prepared diagrams of pyramidal cells (cerebral cortex) and purkinje cells (cerebellum). Both are examples of multipolar neurons of the central nervous system.

   Pyramidal cells were named because of the shape of their cell body in specimens sectioned perpendicular to the brain surface. The apex of the pyramid points to the brain surface. Multiple dendrites emerge from the apex and the corners of the pyramid. A single axon emerges from the base and travels deep into brain tissue.

   Purkinje cells are located in the cortex of the cerebellum between its granular and molecular layers. Purkinje cells have large cell bodies, a massive array of finely branching dendrites that extend towards the surface, and a single small axon that extends into deeper portions of the cerebellum.

4. Observe a diagram of the retina (eye) and locate the bipolar cells. It is fairly easy to identify the bipolar cell nuclei but more difficult to distinctly see the axons and dendrites attached to the cell bodies.

5. Observe a diagram of a spinal cord section and locate the dorsal root ganglion. Located within the dorsal root ganglion are the cell bodies of pseudounipolar neurons. The cell bodies of these neurons are large, rounded with pale cytoplasm and prominent nuclei and nucleoli. The cell bodies are surrounded by a layer of satellite cells.

ACTIVITY 3:

NERVE HISTOLOGY

Resources: Textbook: pages 490-491

Observe a diagram of a nerve in cross section and identify the axon, myelin sheath (if visible), endoneurium, fascicle, perineurium and epineurium.

Materials - Brain

Models and diagrams of the human brain

Sheep brain with meninges intact

Dissecting pan

Dissecting tools: scissors, scalpel, blunt probe, teasing needle, forceps

Bag/tag for storage or bag for disposal

ACTIVITY 4:

Human Brain Anatomy

Resources: Textbook: pages 428-448; 458-461; 492-500

Identify the following structures on diagrams, charts and models of the human brain.

Meninges and Associated Structures

dura mater	arachnoid mater	pia mater
subarachnoid space	arachnoid villi	superior sagittal sinus

Ventricular System

lateral ventricles	interventricular foramen	third ventricle
cerebral aqueduct	fourth ventricle	choroid plexus
septum pellucidum		

Structures of the Cerebrum

gyrus	fissure	sulcus
longitudinal fissure	central sulcus	frontal lobe
parietal lobe	lateral sulcus	temporal lobe
parieto-occipital sulcus	occipital lobe	postcentral gyrus
precentral gyrus	prefrontal cortex	cerebral white matter
olfactory bulbs	olfactory tracts	corpus callosum
optic chiasma	fornix	basal nuclei
cerebral cortex	cerebral hemispheres	

Diencephalon and Associated Structures

pineal gland	epithalamus	thalamus
intermediate mass	hypothalamus	infundibulum
pituitary gland	mammillary bodies	

Brain Stem

corpora quadrigemina	superior colliculi	inferior colliculi
midbrain	pons	medulla oblongata

Cerebellum and Associated Structures

arbor vitae	vermis
transverse fissure	

ACTIVITY 5:

Sheep Brain Dissection

1. Place the sheep brain in the dissection pan, resting on its ventral surface.

2. Examine the **dura mater**, the tough connective tissue layer that is the outer meninx. Using scissors, carefully cut through the dura mater and remove it from your specimen. Be careful when removing the dura from the ventral surface – try to preserve the attachment of the pituitary gland and as many of the cranial nerves as possible.

3. Deep to the dura mater is a filmy, vascular layer called the **arachnoid mater**. Underneath this layer, adhering to the surface of the brain is the **pia mater**.

4. Examine the external features of the sheep brain:

   Cerebrum: This is the most prominent and largest of the brain areas. It is divided by a **longitudinal fissure** into nearly symmetrical **right** and **left cerebral hemispheres**. Gently pull the two hemispheres away from each other and look down into the longitudinal fissure. There you will observe the **corpus callosum**, a band of white, myelinated fibers that connects the two cerebral hemispheres. The surface of each cerebral hemisphere has ridges (convolutions) called **gyri** and depressions which are called either **sulci** (shallow depressions) or **fissures** (deeper depressions). A lateral view of a cerebral hemisphere should enable you to differentiate between the **frontal lobe, parietal lobe, temporal lobe,** and **occipital lobe**.

   Cerebellum: The cerebellum, the second largest brain area, is a rounded structure caudal to the cerebral hemispheres. The cerebellum has smaller gyri that are parallel to each other. Locate the worm-like **vermis**, a short, narrow band of tissue that connects the cerebellar hemispheres.

   Ventral Surface: From this view, you can see the frontal lobes and temporal lobes of the cerebral hemispheres. Observe the **olfactory** bulbs on the ventral surface of the frontal lobes. Locate the **pituitary gland** which is attached to the hypothalamus by a stalk called the **infundibulum**. The **optic chiasma**, an X-shaped junction of fibers at the junction of the **optic** nerves is located anterior to the pituitary gland. Two small rounded processes called **mammillary bodies** are posterior to the pituitary gland; they are part of the hypothalamus.

   Posterior to the mammillary bodies lie the cerebral peduncles, groups of myelinated fibers that are inferior portions of the midbrain. Moving posteriorly, locate the **pons**, clearly seen as a large bulge. Finally, locate the **medulla oblongata** which is caudal to the pons (it looks like a swollen region of the spinal cord). Together, the midbrain, pons and medulla oblongata make up the brainstem.

Corpora Quadrigemina: Hold the specimen in front of you, looking from the posterior to the anterior end, cerebral hemispheres on top. Carefully pull the cerebral hemispheres away from the cerebellum, widening the transverse fissure (do not sever these areas from each other). You may have to tease some connecting tissue away with a probe. A small rounded body called the **pineal gland** should be visible at the midline, nearest the cerebrum. Beneath the pineal gland there are the four bodies of the **corpora quadrigemina** of the midbrain. The two superior bodies, called **superior colliculi** are slightly larger than the two inferior bodies, called **inferior colliculi**.

Internal Structures: Place the brain in the dissecting pan so that the dorsal surface is now facing upward. Using a knife or a long bladed scalpel carefully cut the specimen along the midsagittal line, through the corpus callosum, using the longitudinal fissure as a cutting guide. Now observe the following internal structures:

Locate the **corpus callosum** that was cut through to produce the two midsagittal sections. The fornix is inferior to the corpus callosum. look for the **lateral ventricles** in each brain half, just below the corpus callosum. In the whole brain, they are separated by the **septum pellucidum**. Depending on your cutting plane, the septum pellucidum may still be visible. Try to locate the **choroid plexus** which produces the CSF that fills each ventricle. Also, note the rounded **intermediate mass** which lies in the diencephalon. The intermediate mass is the commissure that connects the nuclei of the **thalamus** and is the only portion of the thalamus that can be seen in this section. It appears as a circle of grey matter surrounded by a shallow section of the third ventricle. The **hypothalamus** includes the tissue located inferior to the thalamus.

Observe the cerebellum. Identify the internal white matter, called the **arbor vitae**. Ventral to the cerebellum is the **fourth ventricle** which is connected to the **third ventricle** by the **cerebral aqueduct** which lies in the midbrain.

Locate these additional structures on the sectioned sheep brain: **medulla oblongata, pons, superior colliculi, inferior colliculi, mammillary bodies, optic chiasma** and **pineal gland**.

Observe the coronal section of the brain on display in the lab. You should be able to see the **cerebral cortex, cerebral nuclei, lateral ventricles, corpus callosum, third ventricle, thalamus** and **hypothalamus.**

5. When you are finished with your dissection, you may save the brain sections using the bags/tags, or dispose of them as directed by your lab instructor.

Checklist:

A. Neuron Structures:

	Model/Diagram	Prepared Slide
Cell body (soma, perikaryon)	_____	_____
Nissl bodies	_____	_____
Nucleus	_____	_____
Nucleolus	_____	_____
Dendrites	_____	_____
Axon Hillock	_____	_____
Axon	_____	_____
Schwann cell	_____	NA
Myelin sheath	_____	_____
Node of Ranvier	_____	_____
Axon collateral	_____	NA
Neurofibril	_____	NA
Neurilemma	_____	NA
Telodendria (Terminal branches)	_____	NA
Axon terminals (synaptic knobs, boutons)	_____	NA

B. Structural Classes of Neurons:

_____ Multipolar neuron (Pyramidal cell)

_____ Multipolar neuron (Purkinje cell)

_____ Bipolar neuron (retina)

_____ Pseudounipolar neuron (dorsal root ganglia)

C. Peripheral Nerve Anatomy:

_____ axon

_____ endoneurium

_____ fascicle

_____ perineurium

_____ epineurium

D. Human Brain Structures:

Meninges and Associated Structures:

_____ dura mater   _____ arachnoid mater   _____ pia mater

_____ subarachnoid space _____ arachnoid villi   _____ superior sagittal sinus

Ventricular System:

_____ lateral ventricles _____ interventricular foramen _____ third ventricle

_____ cerebral aqueduct   _____ fourth ventricle   _____ choroid plexus

_____ septum pellucidum

Structures of the cerebrum:

_____ gyrus   _____ fissure   _____ sulcus

_____ longitudinal fissure   _____ central sulcus   _____ frontal lobe

_____ parietal lobe   _____ lateral sulcus   _____ temporal lobe

_____ parieto-occipital sulcus _____ occipital lobe   _____ postcentral gyrus

_____ precentral gyrus   _____ prefrontal cortex _____ cerebral white matter

_____ olfactory bulbs   _____ olfactory tracts _____ corpus callosum

_____ optic chiasma   _____ fornix   _____ basal nuclei

_____ cerebral cortex   _____ cerebral hemispheres

Diencephalon and Associated Structures:

_____ pineal gland   _____ epithalamus   _____ thalamus

_____ intermediate mass   _____ hypothalamus   _____ infundibulum

_____ pituitary gland   _____ mammillary bodies

Brain Stem:

_____ corpora quadrigemina _____ superior colliculi _____ inferior colliculi

_____ midbrain   _____ pons   _____ medulla oblongata

Cerebellum/Associated Structures:

_____ arbor vitae   _____ vermis   _____ transverse fissure

E. Sheep Brain Dissection

Meninges and Associated Structures:

_____ dura mater   _____ arachnoid mater   _____ pia mater

Ventricular System:

_____ lateral ventricles   _____ interventricular foramen   _____ third ventricle

_____ cerebral aqueduct   _____ fourth ventricle   _____ choroid plexus

_____ septum pellucidum

Structures of the cerebrum:

_____ gyrus   _____ fissure   _____ sulcus

_____ longitudinal fissure   _____ central sulcus   _____ frontal lobe

_____ parietal lobe   _____ lateral sulcus   _____ temporal lobe

_____ occipital lobe   _____ cerebral white matter   _____ olfactory bulbs

_____ olfactory tracts   _____ corpus callosum   _____ optic chiasma

_____ fornix   _____ cerebral nuclei   _____ cerebral cortex

_____ cerebral hemispheres

Diencephalon and Associated Structures:

_____ pineal gland   _____ epithalamus   _____ thalamus

_____ intermediate mass   _____ hypothalamus   _____ infundibulum

_____ pituitary gland   _____ mammillary bodies

Brain Stem:

_____ inferior colliculi   _____ corpora quadrigemina   _____ superior colliculi

_____ medulla oblongata   _____ midbrain   _____ pons

Cerebellum/Associated Structures:

_____ middle cerebellar peduncles   _____ arbor vitae   _____ vermis

_____ superior cerebellar peduncles   _____ inferior cerebellar peduncles

_____ transverse fissure

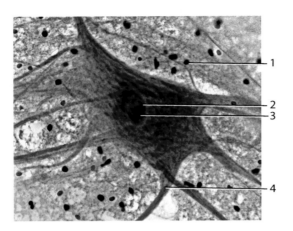

Figure 9.1: Neuron smear.
1) Nucleus of neuron 2) Nucleolus of neuron
3) Dendrites of neuron

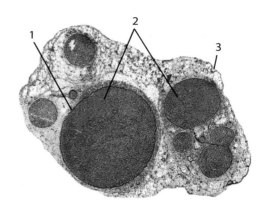

Figure 9.2: Nerve, cross-section. 1) Perineurium
2) Fascicles 3) Epineurium

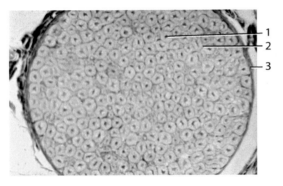

Figure 9.3: Nerve, cross-section. 1) Axon
2) Endoneurium 3) Perineurium

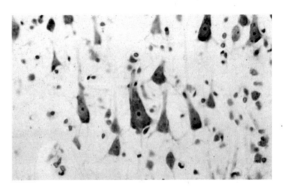

Figure 9.4: Pyramidal cells, cerebral cortex

© bluedoor, LLC

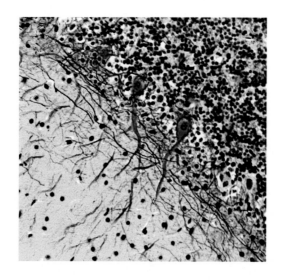

Figure 9.5: Purkinje cells, cerebellum

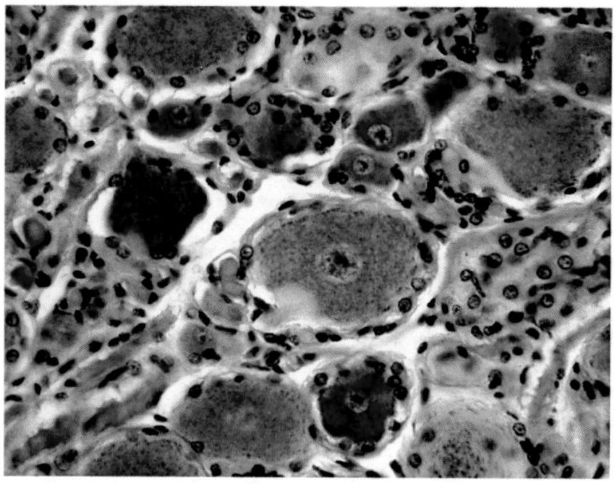

Figure 9.6: Sensory neurons, dorsal root ganglion

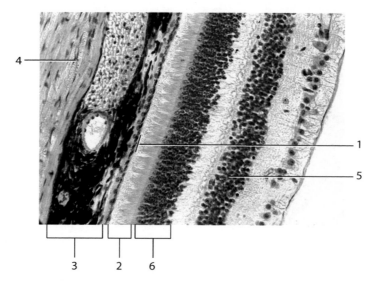

Figure 9.7: Retina. 1) Retina 2) Rods and cones
3) Choroid 4) Sclera 5) Bipolar cell layer
6) nuclei of rods and cones

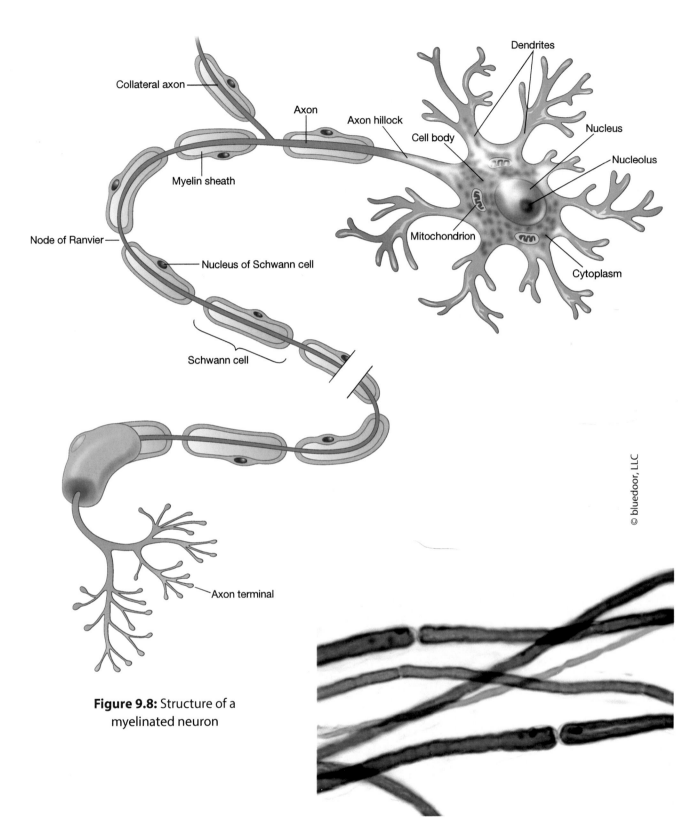

Figures labels:
- Collateral axon
- Axon
- Axon hillock
- Myelin sheath
- Cell body
- Dendrites
- Nucleus
- Nucleolus
- Node of Ranvier
- Nucleus of Schwann cell
- Mitochondrion
- Cytoplasm
- Schwann cell
- Axon terminal

© bluedoor, LLC

Figure 9.8: Structure of a myelinated neuron

Figure 9.9: Axons with nodes of Ranvier

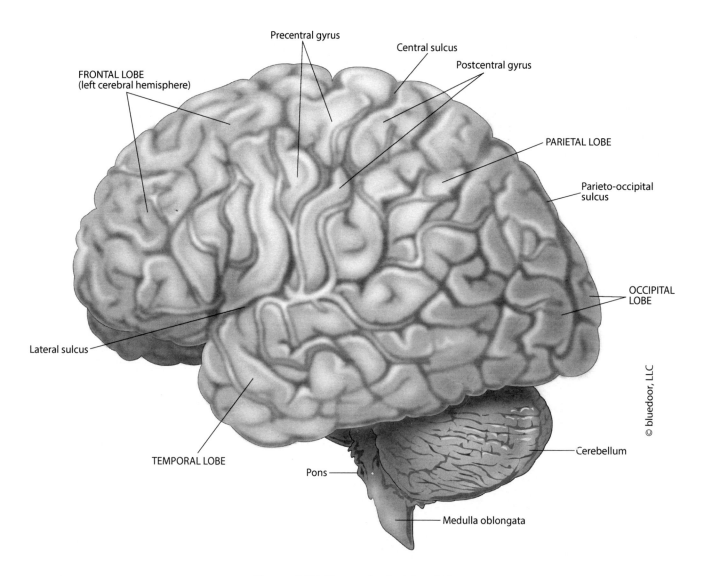

Precentral gyrus

Central sulcus

Postcentral gyrus

FRONTAL LOBE
(left cerebral hemisphere)

PARIETAL LOBE

Parieto-occipital
sulcus

OCCIPITAL
LOBE

Lateral sulcus

© bluedoor, LLC

Cerebellum

TEMPORAL LOBE

Pons

Medulla oblongata

Figure 9.10: Human brain, lateral view

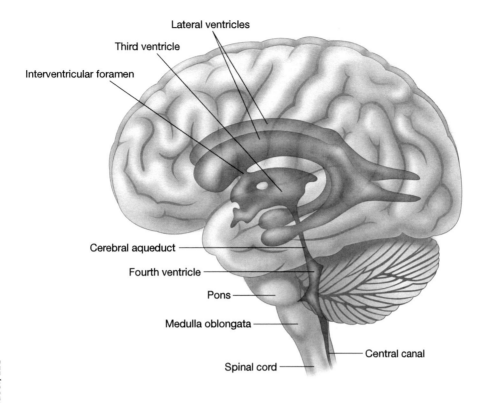

Lateral ventricles

Third ventricle

Interventricular foramen

Cerebral aqueduct

Fourth ventricle

Pons

Medulla oblongata

Central canal

Spinal cord

© bluedoor, LLC

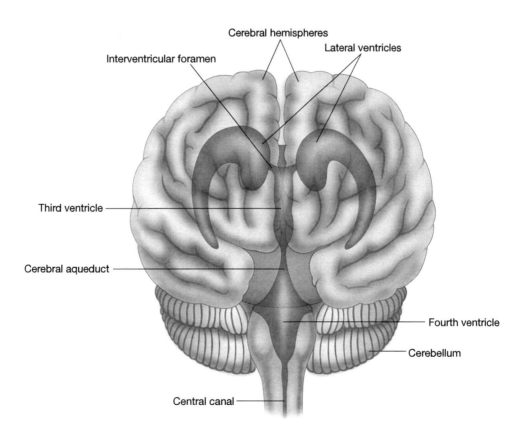

Cerebral hemispheres

Interventricular foramen

Lateral ventricles

Third ventricle

Cerebral aqueduct

Fourth ventricle

Cerebellum

Central canal

Figure 9.11: Ventricles of the brain

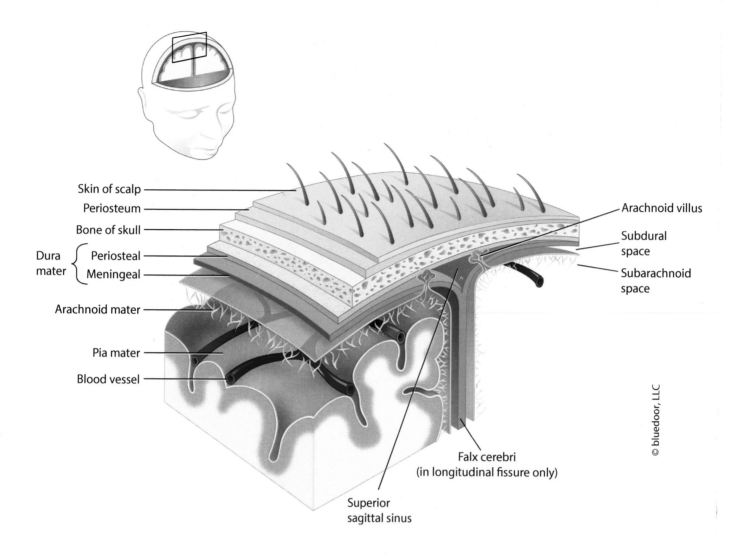

Skin of scalp

Periosteum

Bone of skull

Dura mater {
  Periosteal
  Meningeal
}

Arachnoid mater

Pia mater

Blood vessel

Arachnoid villus

Subdural space

Subarachnoid space

Falx cerebri (in longitudinal fissure only)

Superior sagittal sinus

© bluedoor, LLC

Figure 9.12: Meninges

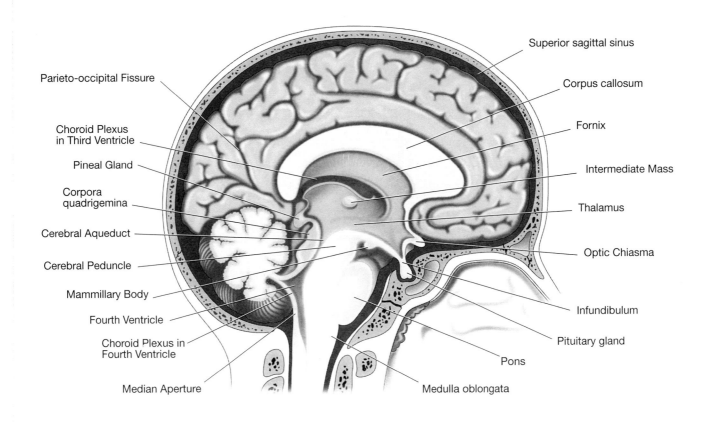

Parieto-occipital Fissure

Choroid Plexus in Third Ventricle

Pineal Gland

Corpora quadrigemina

Cerebral Aqueduct

Cerebral Peduncle

Mammillary Body

Fourth Ventricle

Choroid Plexus in Fourth Ventricle

Median Aperture

Superior sagittal sinus

Corpus callosum

Fornix

Intermediate Mass

Thalamus

Optic Chiasma

Infundibulum

Pituitary gland

Pons

Medulla oblongata

© bluedoor, LLC

Figure 9.13: Human brain, midsaggital view

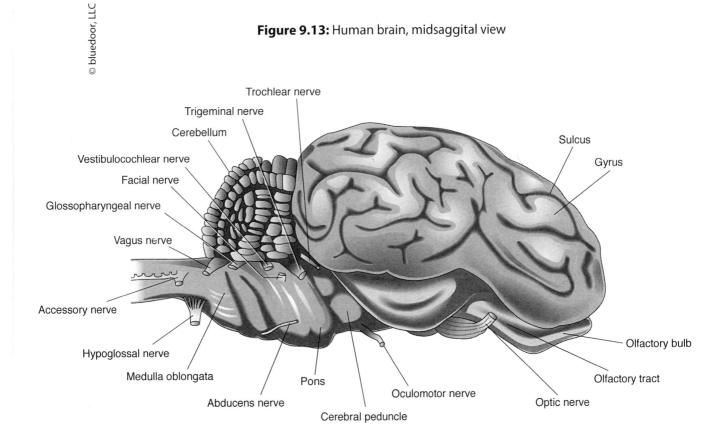

Trochlear nerve

Trigeminal nerve

Cerebellum

Vestibulocochlear nerve

Facial nerve

Glossopharyngeal nerve

Vagus nerve

Accessory nerve

Hypoglossal nerve

Medulla oblongata

Abducens nerve

Pons

Cerebral peduncle

Oculomotor nerve

Optic nerve

Olfactory tract

Olfactory bulb

Sulcus

Gyrus

Figure 9.14: Sheep brain, lateral view

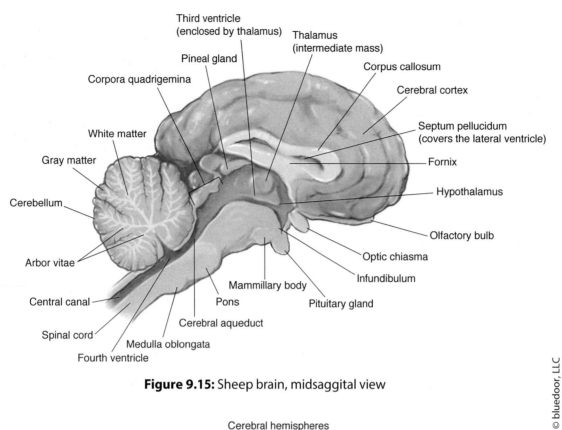

Figure 9.15: Sheep brain, midsaggital view

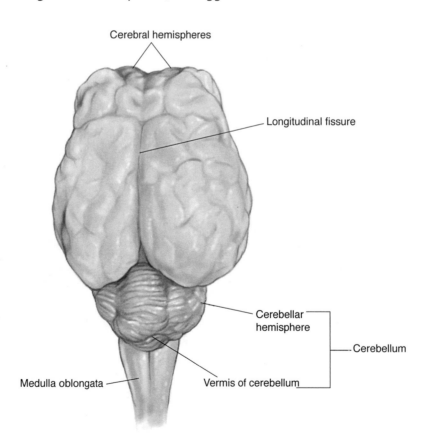

Figure 9.16: Sheep brain, dorsal view

© bluedoor, LLC

Name:

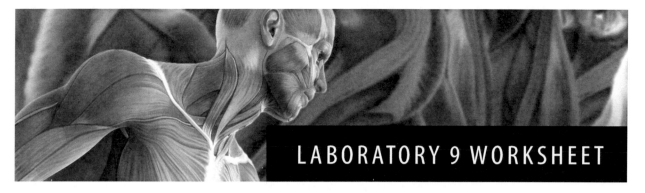

LAB 9 WORKSHEET

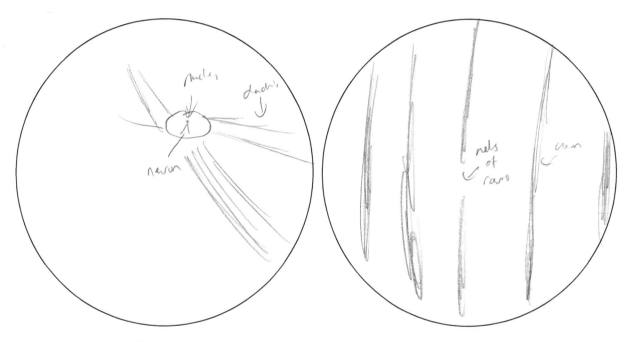

Neuron

Total Magnification: _____

Label the nucleus, soma, nucleolus, and, if possible, axon and dendrites

Nerve Fiber

Total Magnification: 400X

Label the nodes of Ranvier, axon, and neurilemma

1. Match the letters of the diagram of the human brain with the correct label.

_H_ precentral gyrus

_I_ central sulcus

_P_ post central gyrus

_F_ lateral sulcus

_A_ white matter

_D_ pons

_B_ gray matter

_K_ parietal lobe

_E_ temporal lobe

_C_ medulla oblongata

_K_ occipital lobe

_M_ cerebellum

_G_ frontal lobe

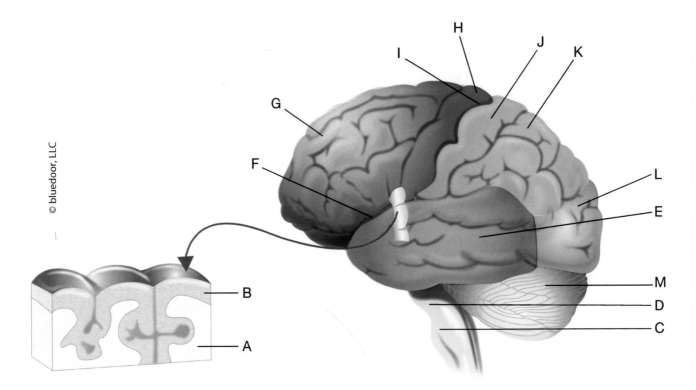

2. Match the letters of the diagram of the human brain with the correct label.

_A_ corpus callosum

_L_ pituitary gland

_O_ cerebral hemisphere

_K_ infundibulum

_N_ intermediate mass

_J_ pons

_C_ choroid plexus

_G_ cerebral aqueduct

_D_ pineal gland

_M_ hypothalamus

_B_ thalamus

_F_ corpora quadrigemina

_E_ arbor vitae

_I_ medulla oblongata

_H_ fourth ventricle

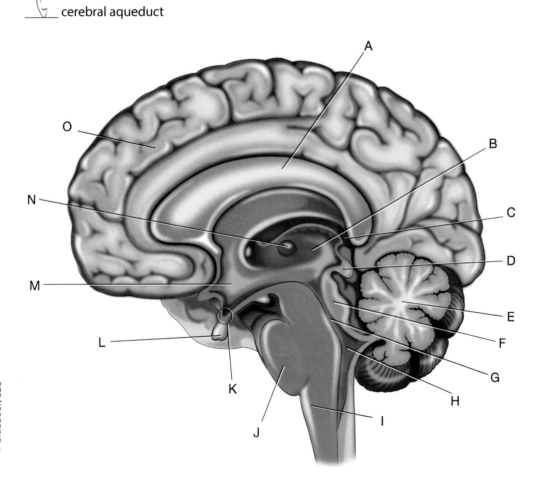

3. Label the structures associated with the circulation of cerebrospinal fluid.

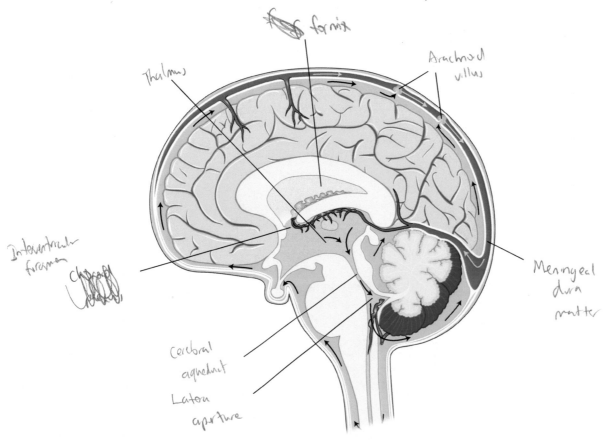

fornix

Thalamus

Arachnoid villus

Interventricular foramen

Choroid plexus

Cerebral aqueduct

Lateral aperture

Meningeal dura matter

4. In what structure of the skull does the pituitary gland sit? Be specific; name the bone and the specific structure of that bone.

Sphenoid   Sella turcica

5. In what structure of the skull do the olfactory bulbs sit? Be specific; name the bone and the specific structure of that bone.

Superior nasal concha.

POST LAB WORKSHEET LAB 9

1. Label the structures of the neuron

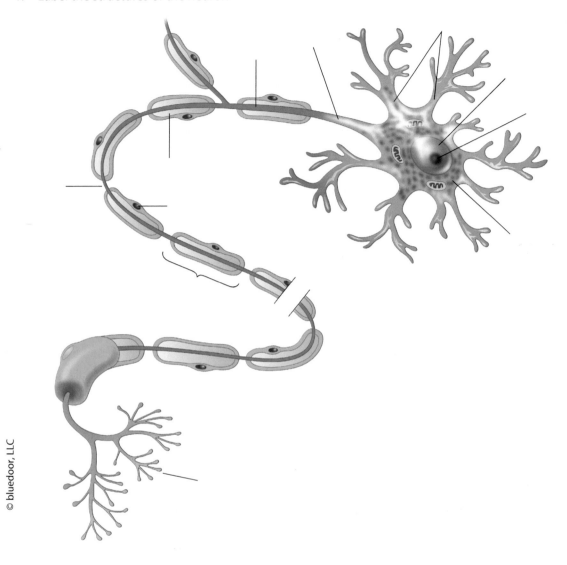

2. Match the term with the description:

a. neurofibril

f. axon

b. Schwann cell

g. telodendria

c. axon hillock

h. node of Ranvier

d. dendrite

i. axon terminal

e. Nissl bodies

j. soma

_____ rough endoplasmic reticulum found in the cell body; also called chromatophilic substance because of its affinity for basic dyes

_____ distal knoblike endings of terminal branches that store neurotransmitter

_____ neuronal process that acts as a receptive area for incoming stimuli

_____ neuroglial cell that surrounds and forms myelin around larger nerve fibers in the peripheral nervous system

_____ biosynthetic center of a neuron; contains the nucleus, nucleolus and ribosomes

_____ terminal branches of an axon

_____ gaps in a myelin sheath

_____ bundles of intermediate filaments that, along with microtubules, help to maintain the shape of a neuron

_____ the cone shaped area of the cell body that gives rise to an axon

_____ neuronal process that generates action potentials and propagates them, typically away from the cell body

3. What is a nerve?

_____

_____

_____

_____

4. Match the term with its description. Each term can be used more than once.

a. multipolar neuron

b. bipolar neuron

c. unipolar neuron (pseudounipolar neuron)

_____ sensory neurons of the peripheral nervous system in which a single process is attached to the cell body; the process divides to form a peripheral process and a central process

_____ major type of neuron in the central nervous system

_____ has two processes attached to the cell body, a single axon and a single dendrite

_____ has a single axon and two or more dendrites attached to the cell body

_____ act as receptor cells for special sense organs, such as the eye and nose

_____ act as motor (efferent) neurons, transmitting impulses away from the central nervous system to effectors

5. What is the location of each nerve connective tissue layer listed below?

Endoneurium: _____

Epineurium: _____

Perineurium: _____

6. In which cerebral lobes would the following functional areas be found?

Primary visual area: _____

Broca's area: _____

Gustatory area: _____

Olfactory area: _____

Primary somatosensory area _____

Primary motor area _____

Premotor area _____

Auditory area _____

7. Using the following terms, match the structure with the description:

cerebral aqueduct	thalamus	diencephalon
corpus callosum	corpora quadrigemina	medulla oblongata
olfactory tract	parietal lobe	cerebellum
hypothalamus	pituitary gland	pineal gland (body)
choroid plexus		

_____ Site of regulation of body temperature and water balance; important ANS center

_____ Sensory perception depends on the function of this area

_____ Encloses the third ventricle

_____ Connects the third ventricle and the fourth ventricle

_____ Located in the midbrain; contains reflex centers for vision and auditory

_____ Regulates posture and coordinates complex muscular movements

_____ Fiber tract concerned with olfaction

_____ Large commissure connecting the cerebral hemispheres

_____ Major relay site for afferent (sensory) impulses traveling to the sensory cortex

_____ Reflex centers for blood pressure, heart rate, salivating and coughing are located here

_____ Connected to the hypothalamus by the infundibulum; an endocrine gland

_____ Located in the diencephalons, this gland secretes melatonin which induces sleep

_____ Produces cerebrospinal fluid (CSF)

8. Identify the meningeal (or associated) structure described below:

Outermost meninx covering the brain; composed of tough fibrous connective tissue

_____

A dural fold that separates the cerebrum from the cerebellum

_____

A dural fold that attaches the cerebrum to the crista gall

_____

Middle meninx

_____

Structure that produces cerebrospinal fluid (CSF)

_____

Innermost meninx covering the brain; delicate and highly vascular

_____

Structures instrumental in returning fluid to the venous blood located in the dural sinuses

_____

Its outer layer forms the periosteum of the skull

_____

9. List in order the structures that cerebrospinal fluid passes through from the lateral ventricles to the dural venous sinuses.

_____

_____

_____

10. Explain why trauma to the base of the brain is often so much more dangerous than trauma to the frontal lobe (hint: which contain centers that are more vital to life)?

_____

_____

_____

11. List the basal nuclei. What is their function?

_____

_____

_____

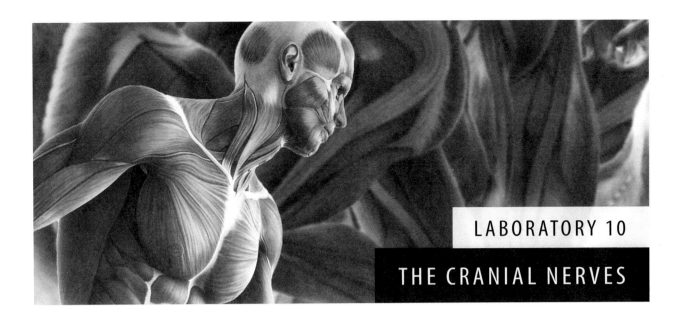

LABORATORY 10

THE CRANIAL NERVES

Objectives

1. Identify the twelve cranial nerves using a human brain model, diagram, and on a sheep brain. Be able to identify them according to name and number.

olfactory nerve (CN I)
Smell

oculomotor nerve (CN III)
eye movement (pup.1)

trigeminal nerve (CN V)
chewing / sensory of face

facial nerve (CN VII)
2/3 taste

glossopharyngeal nerve (CN IX)
1/3 taste more pharynx

accessory nerve (CN XI)
motor neck

optic nerve (CN II)
sight

trochlear nerve (CN IV)
eye move up down

abducens nerve (CN VI)
lateral eye movement

vestibulocochlear nerve (CN VIII)
sound / balance

vagus nerve (CN X)
Same as glosso

hypoglossal nerve (CN XII)
move tongue

2. Identify the foramina through which each cranial nerve exits the cranial cavity.

3. Describe the function of each of the twelve cranial nerves.

4. Assess cranial nerve function by performing cranial nerve assessment tests.

INTRODUCTION

Twelve pairs of cranial nerves are associated with the brain. All but two arise from the brain stem. The cranial nerves innervate structures of the head and neck, with the exception of the vagus nerve which also innervates structures in the thorax and abdomen. Each cranial nerve is represented by a name and Roman numeral (following a cranial-to-caudal sequence).

Some cranial nerves are pure sensory nerves; some are mainly motor while some contain both motor and sensory components. Four cranial nerves also carry parasympathetic fibers.

An important part of a neurological assessment involves testing cranial nerve function. In this laboratory you will perform tests to assess proper functioning of cranial nerves.

Materials

1. Each pair of students should have:

   Sheep brain

   Human skull

2. Class materials to be shared by students:

   Models/diagrams of cranial nerves

   Materials used for cranial nerve testing

ACTIVITY 1:

Cranial nerve anatomy

Resources: Textbook: pages 493

Identify the following cranial nerves on diagrams, charts, models and on the sheep brain:

olfactory nerve (CN I)   optic nerve (CN II)

oculomotor nerve (CN III)   trochlear nerve (CN IV)

trigeminal nerve (CN V)   abducens nerve (CN VI)

facial nerve (CN VII)   vestibulocochlear nerve (CN VIII)

glossopharyngeal nerve (CN IX)   vagus nerve (CN X)

accessory nerve (CN XI)   hypoglossal nerve (CN XII)

ACTIVITY 2:

Foramina associated with cranial nerves

Resources: Textbook: pages 494-500

Identify the foramina through which the cranial nerves pass to exit the cranial cavity. Fill in the chart on your lab worksheet.

ACTIVITY 3:

Tests of cranial nerve function

Resources: Textbook: pages 492-501

Website:

http://classes.kumc.edu/coa/education/AMED900/Neurology/NeurologicalExamination.htm

Olfactory nerve (CN I)

The olfactory nerve is a pure sensory cranial nerve that transmits olfactory information to the brain.

Materials:

Each pair of students should have:

    Vials containing the following:

    vanilla extract

    coffee beans

    alcohol

    small metric ruler

Procedure: Have your lab partner close their eyes and block one nostril by occluding it with their finger. Place the substance vial approximately 10 centimeters below the unobstructed nostril. Ask them to inhale normally and identify the scent. Record their answer on the lab worksheet. Repeat procedure with all vials, alternating nostril tested until both nostrils have been tested using all scents.

Optic nerve (CN II)

The optic nerve is a pure sensory cranial nerve which carries visual information to the brain.

Materials:

Snellen eye chart

Pencil or pen

Procedure: Examination of the optic nerve involves a determination of visual acuity and peripheral vision.

Visual acuity: Acuity is the sharpness of a visual image. Use the Snellen eye chart located on the lab wall to perform this test. Record your observations on the lab worksheet.

1. Have the subject stand 20 feet (6.1 m) away from and facing the chart.

2. Have the subject cover one eye and read the letters on the chart as you point to them, starting with the top line and working to the bottom.

3. Note the lowest row of letters that can be read accurately. Record the number of that row in the worksheet (use the bottom number in the ratio printed to the left of the row of letters). That number is the farthest distance (in feet) that a person with normal acuity can see the letters in that row. For example, if a subject has 20-20 vision, that subject can see at 20 feet what a person with normal vision can see at 20 feet. If the number is 20-40, the subject sees at 20 feet what a normal subject can see at 40 feet. Test with both eyes and record the numbers; if the subject wears glasses, you can try it both ways (make sure to note in your worksheet whether the subject wore glasses or not during the test).

   Peripheral vision: This test assesses your peripheral or side vision. Have your lab partner sit directly in front of you at the same eye level height and at a distance of about 2 feet. Have them cover their right eye and look directly at you with their left eye. Make sure they continue to stare directly ahead during this procedure. Place a pencil on their left side to a point where they cannot see the pencil. Move the pencil in an arc toward the student's nose. Have them report when they first see the pencil. Estimate the angle from the center of the pupil to the point at which the pencil was detected. Repeat with the other eye. Record your observations on the lab worksheet.

Oculomotor (CN III)

Six extrinsic eye muscles are responsible for eye movements. Three cranial nerves control these muscles. Four of these six muscles are controlled by the oculomotor nerve, which include the superior rectus, inferior rectus and medial rectus and the inferior oblique muscles.

Materials:

Each pair of students should have:

Penlight

Pen or pencil

Centimeter ruler

Procedure to test for motor functions: Stand directly in front of the student to be tested. Ask them to stare directly ahead. Have the student follow with their eyes as you trace the letter H in space. Look for smooth coordinated movement with both eyes. Record your observations in the lab worksheet.

The oculomotor nerve controls the levator palpebrae superioris muscle that raises the upper eyelid. Ask your lab partner to stare directly ahead. Check the position of each eyelid. Normally about one third of the iris of the eye should be covered by the eyelid. Record your observations on the worksheet.

The oculomotor nerve also carries parasympathetic fibers to control the sphincter pupillae. Activation of this smooth muscle causes pupil constriction. The ciliary muscle also receives parasympathetic fibers via the oculomotor nerve. This muscle is responsible for lens accommodation for close vision.

Procedure to test for pupillary constriction: As your lab partner is looking directly ahead look to see if both pupils are the same size. Are they round or oval? Are they facing forward? For the next procedure move to a dimly lit area. Have your lab partner focus on an object in the distance straight ahead. Hold the penlight about 20 centimeters to the side of the eye and direct the light toward the pupil. Did the pupil constrict? Was the response seen in both pupils simultaneously? Record your observations.

Procedure to test for accommodation: Have your lab partner stare straight ahead at a distant object. Take a pencil and place it about 1 meter in front of your lab partner's gaze. Have your lab partner follow the pencil as you move the pencil to about 3 centimeters in front of their nose. Look for convergence of the eyes as the subject follows the path of the moving pencil. Record your observations.

Trochlear nerve (CN IV)

The trochlear nerve is a pure motor nerve which supplies one of the six extrinsic eye muscles, the superior oblique. The action of this muscle is to bring the eye downward and inward.

Procedure to test for motor function: Have your lab partner look down at the tip of their nose. Observe the movement in both eyes. Is the movement symmetrical and smooth? Record your observations.

Trigeminal nerve (CN V)

The trigeminal nerve has both motor and sensory components. The motor fibers control the muscles of mastication and the sensory fibers convey the sensations of pain, touch, temperature and pressure from the face, eyes, gums, oral and nasal mucosa, teeth and the anterior two thirds of the tongue. There are three major divisions of the trigeminal nerve: the ophthalmic, maxillary, and mandibular.

Materials:

Each pair of students should have:

> Von Frey hair
>
> Cold and warm mall probe
>
> Disposable tongue depressor

Procedure to test motor functions of the trigeminal nerve: Ask your lab partner to clench their teeth several times. While you lab partner is clenching their teeth palpate the temporalis muscle on each side of the head. Is the contraction of equal strength on each side? Ask your lab partner to bite down on a tongue depressor on the right side. Try and pull the tongue depressor out. Repeat this procedure on the opposite side. Record your observations.

Procedure to test sensory functions of trigeminal nerve: Three divisions of the trigeminal nerve will be tested for sensory function. To test the ophthalmic division (V1) perform the described procedures on the forehead just above the glabella slightly to the left and slightly to the right. The maxillary division (V2) is tested on the skin of the buccal region on the left side and then on the right side. The mandibular division (V3) is tested on the mental region slightly to the left side then slightly to the right side. See figure below. With your lab partner's eyes closed, take the Von Frey hair and touch the skin lightly in several different locations. Ask them to indicate if they feel the touch. Repeat this procedure with the cold mall probe and the warm mall probe. Record your observations.

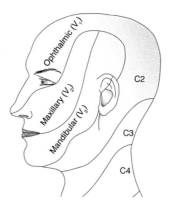

Sensory distribution of the three divisions of the trigeminal nervte

Abducens nerve (CN VI)

The abducens nerve is a pure motor nerve which supplies one of the six extrinsic eye muscles, the lateral rectus. The action of this muscle is to abduct the eye (move it laterally)

Procedure to test for motor function: Have your lab partner stare straight ahead and then move the eyes to the right and then to the left. Observe the movement in both eyes. Is the movement symmetrical and smooth? Record your observations.

Facial nerve (CN VII)

The facial nerve is a mixed cranial nerve that also has parasympathetic fibers associated with it. The motor component controls the muscles of facial expression. The sensory portion conveys taste information from the taste buds located on the anterior two-thirds of the tongue. Parasympathetic fibers innervate the submandibular and sublingual salivary glands, the lacrimal (tear) glands of the eyes, and nasal and palatine glands.

Materials:

Each pair of students should have:

> sugar solution
>
> salt solution
>
> 8 disposable pipets

Procedure to test motor component of the facial nerve: Ask you lab partner to smile, lift their eyebrows, frown, close their eyes tightly, pucker their lips, and wrinkle the forehead. Look for symmetry of the muscles on both sides of the face.

Procedure to test for sensory function of the facial nerve: Ask your lab partner to close their eyes and protrude their tongue. Place a few drops of sugar or salt solution on the anterior half of the tongue on the right side. Have your lab partner raise their hand when they taste the solution. Have them report which solution was placed on their tongue. Repeat these steps until both sides of the tongue are tested for both solutions. Record your observations.

Vestibulocochlear nerve (CN VIII)

The vestibulocochlear nerve is a pure sensory nerve that conveys sound information and balance (equilibrium).

Materials:

Tuning forks, rubber mallet

A. **Rinne Test:** This test is used to identify impairment in the conduction of sound though the external and middle ear, to the sensory areas of the inner ear. It is done by comparing air conduction with bone conduction.

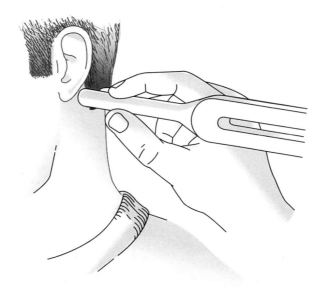

© bluedoor, LLC

1. Strike a tuning fork with a rubber mallet and place its handle on the subject's mastoid process.

2. When the subject no longer hears the sound, move the prongs (they should be vibrating) to the opening of the external auditory meatus; be careful not to touch it. Normally, a hum will be heard again; if not, conduction impairment is suspected. Record your results in the worksheet.

3. Repeat on the other side of the head.

B. **Weber Test.** This is another test used to identify defects in conduction. The Weber Test is only useful if there is an asymmetrical hearing loss. If hearing is symmetrical, the patient perceives the sound in the middle of their head.

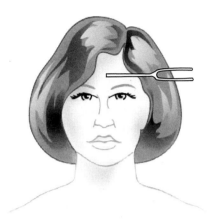

© bluedoor, LLC

1. Strike a tuning fork with a rubber mallet and place the handle against the middle of the subject's forehead.

2. Ask the subject on which side, if any, the sound seems louder.

C. **Romberg Test:** The Romberg test evaluates a subject's ability to maintain balance and equilibrium, using proprioceptors and the vestibular apparatus (utricle and saccule) without the aid of vision. Impairment of the dorsal white column of the spinal cord (transmits information from proprioceptors to the brain), the vestibular apparatus, the basal ganglia or the cerebellum can be detected during this test. Note: If equilibrium impairment exists, the subject may topple over. Have at least one person standing by to stabilize the subject if this happens.

1. Have the subject stand near a blackboard, facing away from it.

2. Draw a line on each side the subject's body, parallel to it.

3. Have the subject stand in place with their eyes open, staring straight ahead for 2 minutes. Note any swaying movements, using the lines on the board as a reference.

4. Repeat the test, this time with the subject's eyes closed. Again, note the degree of side-to-side movement.

5. Repeat the test again (steps 3 and 4 above) with the subject standing perpendicular to the board (the left shoulder is near the board, but not touching it)

Glossopharyngeal nerve (CN IX) and Vagus nerve (CN X)

The glossopharyngeal nerve is a mixed nerve that also supplies parasympathetic innervation to the parotid salivary glands in the head. The motor fibers of the glossopharyngeal supply skeletal muscles of the pharynx, larynx, and soft palate. Sensory fibers convey taste information from taste buds on the posterior one third of the tongue. Sensory information concerning blood pressure and blood chemistry is also found in this cranial nerve.

The vagus is also a mixed nerve with parasympathetic fibers. The parasympathetic fibers innervate structures in the neck, thorax and into the abdomen. The motor fibers of the vagus supply skeletal muscles of the pharynx and larynx. Some taste buds are found around the epiglottis. Sensory information from these taste buds is conveyed by the vagus nerve.

Many functions of the glossopharyngeal and vagus nerves overlap; therefore, typically these two nerves are tested together.

Materials:

Materials to be shared by pairs of students:

> Disposable tongue depressors
>
> Disposable cotton-tipped applicators
>
> penlight
>
> Sugar and salt solutions
>
> 8 disposable pipettes

Procedure: Ask your lab partner to open their mouth and say "ahh". Look at the position of the soft palate and uvula before and during the test. During phonation the uvula should rise in the midline position. Record your observations.

Ask your lab partner to swallow. Do they have any difficulties? Ask them to read a sentence from the lab manual. Is there any unexplained hoarseness?

Next test the gag reflex. Have your lab partner protrude their tongue. Gently depress the tongue with the tongue depressor and lightly touch the back of the throat on the right side with the cotton-tip applicator. Repeat this procedure and test the gag reflex on the left side. Record your observations.

To test the taste functions of the glossopharyngeal nerve, repeat the test you performed for the facial nerve on the posterior aspect of the tongue. Record your observations.

Accessory nerve (CN XI)

The accessory nerve has primarily motor function; it transmits motor fibers to the sternocleidomastoid and trapezius muscles.

Procedure: Have your lab partner stare straight ahead. Place your hand on their right cheek. Have them turn their head to the right against the resistance of your hand. Repeat this procedure on the left side. For each side, assess the strength of the muscle contraction using a scale of 1 (very weak) to

4 (very strong). Observe whether there are any differences in the strength of the muscle contraction between the two sides. Record your observations.

Have your lab partner sit up straight on the lab stool. Place your hands on their shoulders. Ask them to shrug their shoulders against resistance. Assess the strength of the contraction using the scale mentioned above. Compare the strength of the contraction between the two sides and record your observations.

Hypoglossal nerve (CN XII)

The hypoglossal nerve is primarily a motor nerve to the intrinsic muscles of the tongue.

Procedure: Ask your lab partner to protrude their tongue in the midline. Look for any deviations to the right or left. The tongue should not deviate from the midline. Record your observations.

Checklist:

A. Cranial nerves

	Model/Diagram	Sheep brain	Foramina	Function/Testing
Olfactory	_____	_____	_____	_____
Optic	_____	_____	_____	_____
Oculomotor	_____	_____	_____	_____
Trochlear	_____	_____	_____	_____
Trigeminal	_____	_____	_____	_____
Abducens	_____	_____	_____	_____
Facial	_____	_____	_____	_____
Vestibulocochlear	_____	_____	_____	_____
Glossopharyngeal	_____	_____	_____	_____
Vagus	_____	_____	_____	_____
Accessory	_____	_____	_____	_____
Hypoglossal	_____	_____	_____	_____

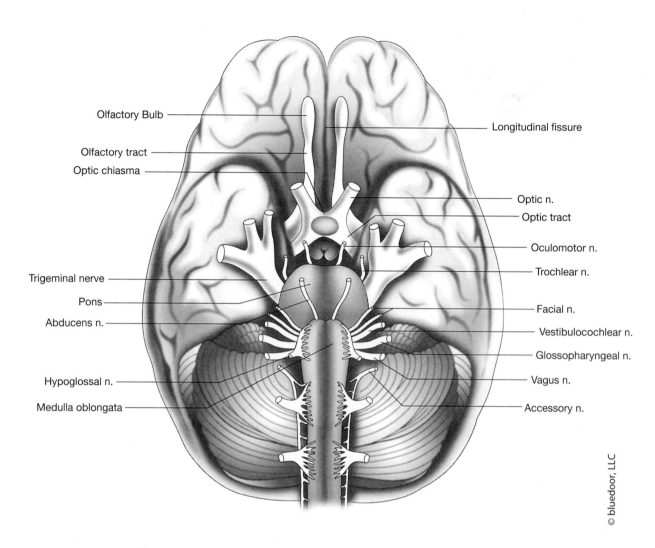

Figure 10.1: Human brain, inferior view, illustrating cranial nerves

© bluedoor, LLC

CRANIAL NERVE ASSESSMENT REPORT

Instructors initials _____

Name: _____

Date: _____

I. Olfactory Nerve

Odor	Right Nostril (yes or no)	Left Nostril (yes or no)
Vanilla extract	No	Yes
Coffee	Yes	Yes
Alcohol	Yes	Yes

II. Optic Nerve

A. Visual Acuity (Snellen test):

Without glasses	right eye:_____	left eye:_____
With glasses (if applicable)	right eye:___8___	left eye:___8___

B. Peripheral Vision:

Quadrant	Upper	Lower	Left	Right
Left eye	40	140	30	150
Right eye	40	140	30	150

III. Oculomotor nerve

A. Able to track H shape with both eyes   yes __✓__   no _____

B. Eyelid position

Right eye   normal __✓__   drooping _____

Left eye   normal __✓__   drooping _____

C. Pupil size and shape

Right and left pupil equal size   yes __✓__   no _____

Right pupil   round __✓__   oval _____

Left pupil   round __✓__   oval _____

D. Pupillary reflex   present __✓__   absent _____

Consensual   yes __✓__   no _____

E. Accommodation   yes __✓__   no _____

IV. Trochlear nerve

Able to look at the tip of the nose

right eye   normal __✓__   abnormal _____

left eye   normal __✓__   abnormal _____

V. Trigeminal nerve

A. Temporalis contraction strength—Right equals left?   yes __✓__   no _____

Masseter contraction strength—Right equals left?   yes __✓__   no _____

B. Sensory functions

Division	Light touch (yes/no)		Cold (yes/no)		Warm (yes/no)	
	Right side	Left side	Right side	Left side	Right side	Left side
Ophthalmic	✓	✓	✓	✓	✓	✓
Maxillary	✓	✓	✓	✓	✓	✓
Mandibular	✓	✓	✓	✓	✓	✓

VI. Abducens nerve

Able to abduct the eye (turn eye laterally)

right eye   normal __✓__ abnormal _____

left eye   normal __✓__ abnormal _____

VII. Facial nerve

A. Muscles of facial expression

Facial expression	Symmetrical (Yes or no)	Normal (Yes or no)
Smile	Yes	
Lift eyebrows	Yes	
Frown	Yes	
Close eyes tightly	Yes	
Pucker lips	Yes	
Wrinkle forehead	Yes	

B. Taste function

Solution	Right side of the tongue (Yes or no)	Left side of the tongue (Yes or no)
Sugar	✓	✓
Salt	✓	✓

VIII. Vestibulocochlear nerve

A. Rhine test

Conduction	Right ear (Yes or no)	Left ear (Yes or no)
Bone	✓	✓
Air	✓	✓

B. Weber test

Is the sound heard equally in both ears?   yes ✓   no _____

C. Romburg test

Describe the results of this test.

_____

_____

_____

IX and X. Glossopharyngeal and vagus nerve

A. Phonation test (say ahh)

Uvula and palate rise in midline?   yes ✓   no _____

Deviation to the right or left?   yes _____   no ✓

B. Speech

Vocalization normal?   yes _____   no ✓

C. Swallowing

Swallowing normal?   yes ✓   no _____

D. Gag reflex

Present on the right side?   yes ✓   no _____

Present on the left side?   yes ✓   no _____

E. Taste

Solution	Right side of the tongue (Yes or no)	Left side of the tongue (Yes or no)
Sugar	✓	✓
Salt	✓	✓

XI. Accessory nerve

A. Strength of sternocleidomastoid muscle (0, very weak to 4, very strong)

Right _3_   Left _3_

B. Strength of trapezius muscle (0, very weak to 4, very strong)

Right _3_   Left _3_

XII. Hypoglossal nerve

A. Protrusion of the tongue

Normal ✓   deviation to the right _____   deviation to the left _____

Name:_____

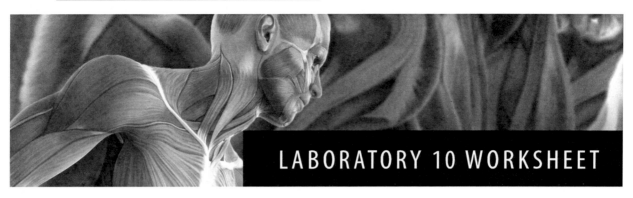

LAB 10 WORKSHEET

1. Provide the name and number of each cranial nerve listed below:

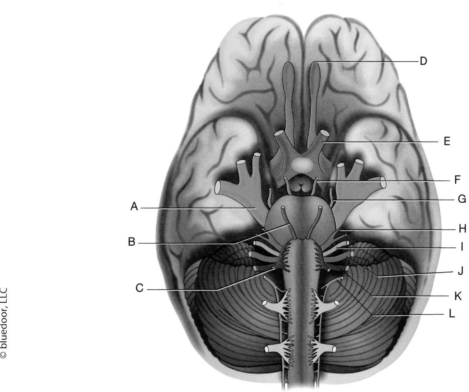

© bluedoor, LLC

A. ___Trigeminal (V)___

B. ___A̶c̶c̶e̶s̶s̶ Abducens (VI)___

C. ___Hypoglossal (XII)___

D. ___olfactory (I)___

E. ___optic (II)___

F. ___Oculomotor (III)___

G. ___Trochlear (IV)___

H. ___Facial (VII)___

I. ___V̶a̶g̶u̶ Vestibulocochlear (VIII)___

J. ___Glossopharygeal (IX)___

K. ___Vagus (X)___

L. ___Accessory (XI)___

2. Complete the following table.

Cranial Nerve Name	Number	Associated foramina
Olfactory		
Optic		
Oculomotor		
Trochlear		
Trigeminal		
ophthalmic branch	V1	
maxillary branch	V2	
mandibular branch	V3	
Abducens		
Facial		
Vestibulocochlear		
Glossopharyngeal		
Vagus		
Accessory		
Hypoglossal		

3. For most cranial nerves tested you performed the test on the right side and the left side. Why was it necessary to do this?

_____

_____

4. Name the three cranial nerves that carry taste fibers:

_____

_____

_____

5. Name three cranial nerves that control the movements of the eye:

_____

_____

_____

6. You have a patient with an absent gag reflex. What test would you perform to determine if the cranial nerve that is involved is the glossopharyngeal or the vagus? Explain your reasoning!

_____

_____

_____

_____

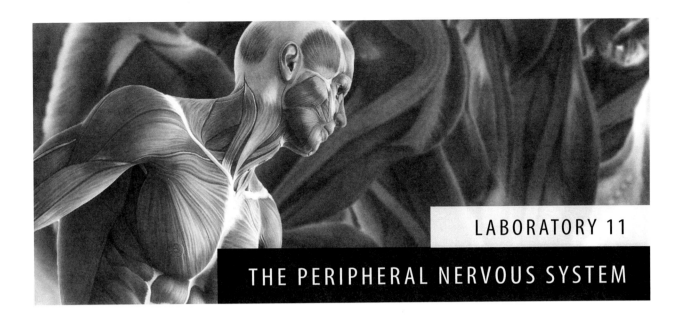

Objectives

1. Identify the following structures of the spinal cord and spinal nerves using models, slides and/or diagrams

Anterior funiculus	Lateral funiculus	Posterior funiculus	Central canal
Anterior median fissure	Posterior median sulcus	Grey commissure	dura mater
Arachnoid mater	Pia mater	Dorsal root ganglion	Dorsal root
Ventral root	Lateral horn	Posterior horn	Anterior horn
Ventral ramus	Dorsal ramus		

2. Identify each of the four nerve plexuses using diagrams or models, and also identify the major nerves associated with them.

Cervical plexus	Phrenic nerve
Brachial plexus	axillary nerve, radial nerve, ulnar nerve, median nerve, musculocutaneous nerve
Lumbar plexus	Femoral nerve, obturator nerve
Sacral plexus	sciatic nerve, fibular (common peroneal) nerve, tibial nerve

3. Define the following terms **reflex** and **reflex arc** and identify the structures of a reflex arc and their functions. Complete the exercises on human reflex physiology as directed by the instructor.

INTRODUCTION

The spinal cord is one of the two major organs of the central nervous system. It extends from the foramen magnum to the level of L1 or L2 vertebra. It carries information to and from the brain and also mediates spinal reflexes.

The spinal cord is enclosed by the three-layered connective tissue sheath called **meninges**.

Dura mater is the tough, outer, single-layered membrane. It is superficial to the **arachnoid** mater (spider-web like). Between these two layers is the subdural space. The innermost delicate and vascular layer which abuts the spinal cord is the **pia mater**. Between the pia mater and arachnoid mater is the subarachnoid space filled with cerebrospinal fluid. There are 31 pairs of spinal nerves that emerge from the spinal cord, pass through the intervertebral foramina and serve the appropriate body area. Spinal nerves are named for the vertebral region and level from which they arise.

In the transverse section of the spinal cord the most visible parts are the gray matter and white matter. The gray matter is an 'H' shaped area or butterfly shaped area in the center surrounded by areas of white matter. The gray matter consists of neuronal cell bodies and dendrites while the white matter is composed of myelinated fibers. In this lab you will also be able to identify other structures in the gray matter and white matter and also learn how the spinal nerves branch and form plexuses (networks). The fibers from different spinal nerves are reorganized to form many peripheral nerves.

Reflexes are rapid, involuntary responses to a stimulus. The nerve impulse usually travels through a pathway, the **reflex arc** from receptor to effector. Reflexes can be classified as somatic if they activate skeletal muscle and as autonomic if they activate smooth or cardiac muscle or glands. Somatic reflexes mediated by the spinal cord are called spinal reflexes. In this lab a series of reflex testing will also be done. Clinically it helps one to evaluate the nervous system and to diagnose any dysfunction or abnormality.

Materials

1. Each student should have a compound microscope

2. Each pair of students should have:

    Prepared slides of cross-section of spinal cord

3. Class materials to be shared by students:

    Models/diagrams of spinal cord and plexuses

    Materials used for reflex testing

ACTIVITY 1:

Spinal cord / Spinal nerve anatomy

Resources: Textbook: pages 464 – 473

Identify the following structures of the spinal cord and spinal nerves using models, slides and/or diagrams:

Anterior funiculus	Lateral funiculus	Posterior funiculus	Central canal
Anterior median fissure	Posterior median sulcus	Grey commissure	dura mater
Arachnoid mater	Pia mater	Dorsal root ganglion	Dorsal root
Ventral root	Lateral horn	Posterior horn	Anterior horn
Ventral ramus	Dorsal ramus		

The spinal cord is partially divided into a right and left half by an **anterior median fissure** and a **posterior median sulcus** (shallower). The gray matter is located in the center and white matter outside. The **central canal** contains cerebrospinal fluid.

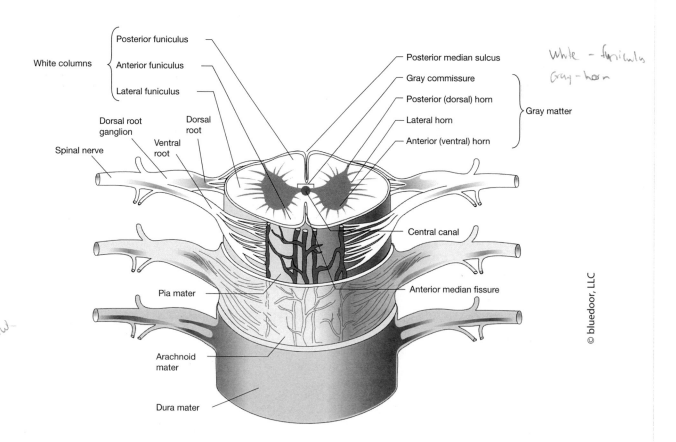

White — funiculus
Gray — horn

Twle
Facal
Synaptal-

Spinal roots / spinal nerves / rami

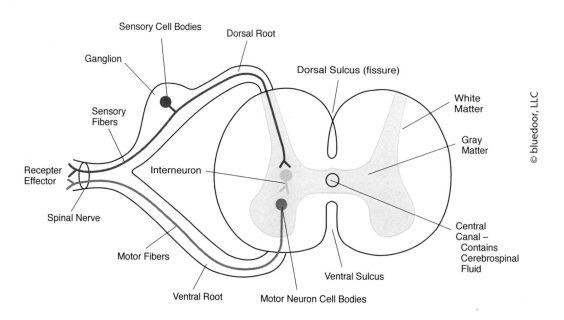

Dorsal root of spinal cord is formed by afferent fibers (sensory) that carry impulses from peripheral receptors

Dorsal root ganglion is an area of the gray matter in the dorsal root, which consists of neuron cell bodies.

Ventral root of spinal cord is formed by efferent fibers (motor) that carry impulses to the effectors (skeletal muscles)

Spinal nerves are formed from the merging of dorsal (posterior) root and ventral (anterior) root. They contain both sensory fibers and motor fibers and are therefore **mixed nerves**

Outside the spinal cavity each spinal nerve branches to form a **ventral ramus** and a **dorsal ramus**. The rami contain mixed nerve fibers like the short spinal nerves. The fibers of the ventral ramus branch and form a network of nerves (plexus).

ACTIVITY 2:

Nerve plexuses

Resources: Textbook: pages 501 - 509

Identify each of the four nerve plexuses using models or diagrams and also identify the major nerves associated with each plexus.

Cervical plexus	Phrenic nerve
Brachial plexus	Axillary nerve, radial nerve, ulnar nerve, median nerve, musculocutaneous nerve
Lumbar plexus	Femoral nerve, obturator nerve
Sacral plexus	Sciatic nerve, fibular (common peroneal) nerve, tibial nerve

There are 31 pairs of spinal nerves (mixed nerves). The dorsal rami of these nerves supply the posterior body trunk. The ventral rami supply the other parts of the trunk and the limbs. The ventral rami of spinal nerves T_2 through T_{12} continue as the intercostal nerves. All the other ventral rami join to form plexuses (a network of nerves). These are the cervical plexus (C_1 through C_5), brachial plexus (C_5 through C_8 and T_1), lumbar plexus (L_1 through L_4) and sacral plexus (L_4 through S_4). The thoracic spinal nerves (T_2 through T_{12}) do not participate in forming plexuses and continue as intercostal nerves.

ACTIVITY 3:

Human reflex physiology

Resources: Textbook: pages 513-518

Define **reflex** and **reflex arc**. Identify the structures of the following patellar stretch reflexes and their functions. Classify each reflex as somatic or autonomic. Complete the exercises on human reflex physiology.

Reflex arc:

1. receptor   – site of stimulus

2. sensory neuron   – carries the afferent impulses to CNS

3. Integration center   – located within the gray matter of CNS and relays information from sensory neuron to motor neuron

4. motor neuron   – carries the efferent impulses to the effector

5. effector   – is a muscle (skeletal, smooth or cardiac) or a gland

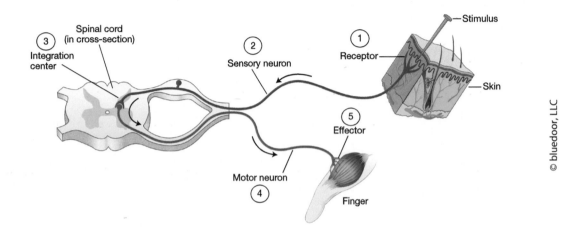

© bluedoor, LLC

Reflexes can be monosynaptic (one synapse reflex) where the afferent neuron synapses directly with the efferent neuron or polysynaptic which involves more than one synapse.

Spinal reflexes (e.g. patellar reflex) are integrated at the spinal cord level rather than at the higher brain centers. Other reflexes require higher brain centers (e.g. pupillary light reflex)

I. Stretch reflex (patellar reflex)

These reflexes help to maintain posture, balance, and movement. When a tendon is tapped the muscle to which the tendon is attached is stretched. The muscle spindles are stimulated and a contraction occurs in the stretched muscle. The antagonistic muscles are inhibited. They relax and prevent the reversal of the contraction.

Testing the patellar reflex:

Start the Software

1. Click on the LabScribe shortcut on the computer's desktop to open the program. If a shortcut is not available, click on the Windows Start menu, move the cursor to All Programs and then to the listing for iWorx. Select LabScribe from the iWorx submenu. The LabScribe Main window will appear as the program opens.

2. On the Main window, pull down the Settings menu and select Load Group.

3. Locate the folder that contains the settings group, IFHPLMv1.iwxgrp. Select this group and click Open.

4. Pull down the Settings menu again. Select the PlatellarStretchReflex-LS2 settings file.

5. After a short time, LabScribe will appear on the computer screen as configured by the Patellar Stretch reflex LS2 settings.

Attach the electrodes to the subject

1. Use an alcohol swab to clean and abrade three regions on the medial thigh of the left leg for electrode attachment. One area is posterior to the medial side of the knee, the second is in the about 12 cm from the knee, and the third area is 10 cm above the former area. Let the areas dry.

2. Remove the plastic disk from a disposable electrode and apply it to one of the abraded areas. Repeat for the other two areas.

3. Attach three color-coded electrode leads to the ground and Channel 1 inputs on the lead pedestal and snap the other ends into the disposable electrodes so that:

   • the black (-1) lead wire is attached to an electrode which is about 12cm from the knee.

   • the red (+1) lead wire is attached to an electrode which is about 10cm above the negative electrode.

   • the green (C) lead wire is attached to the electrode on the medial side of the knee (see Figure 2 above)

Procedure

1. Instruct the subject to sit on a lab bench so that the subject's thighs are supported by the top of the bench and his or her calves hang freely.

2. Feel the position of the patellar tendon just below the kneecap. Place one hand on the patella (kneecap), and use the other hand to tap the patellar tendon with the reflex hammer. Find the point on the patellar tendon that causes the greatest response from the quadriceps muscle. Mark this spot with a marker.

3. Click Record and then instruct the subject to raise and lower his or her lower leg to demonstrate the type of EMG that occurs during quadriceps contraction and relaxation. Click AutoScale on the EMG Quad channel. Click Stop to halt the recording

4. Type baseline in the Mark box that is to the right of the Mark button. Click Record. Press the Enter key on the keyboard to mark the recording.

5. Instruct the subject to relax his or her quadriceps muscle and that the exercise has begun.

6. Tap the subject's patellar tendon to elicit the stretch reflex. Record a total of ten trials using the same tapping force.

7. After the tenth trial, click Stop to halt recording.

8. Repeat this exercise on the same subject to test the effect of mental distraction. Ask the subject to mentally perform two or three digit subtraction problems. At the same time do the patellar reflex test again.

Data Analysis

1. Scroll to the beginning of the data recorded for Exercise 1 to display the first trial on the Main window.

2. Click on the Analysis window icon in the toolbar (Figure 1) or select Analysis from the Windows menu to transfer the data displayed in the Main window to the Analysis window (Figure 2).

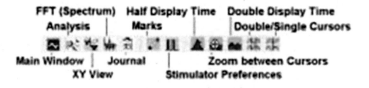

Figure 1. Toolbar

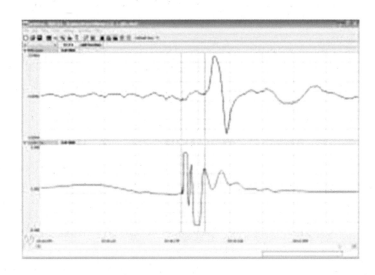

Figure 2. Analysis window

3. Look at the Function Table that is above the display of the EMG Quad channel displayed in the Analysis window. The mathematical function, T2-T1, should appear in this table. The value for T2-T1 is seen in the table across the top margin of the EMG Quad channel.

4. Use the mouse to click on and drag a cursor to the onset of the signal recorded from plethysmograph on the reflex hammer, which is displayed on the Tendon Tap channel. Drag the other cursor to the beginning of the EMG wave which is recorded on the EMG Quad channel.

5. The functions in the channel pull-down menus of the Analysis window can be used to enter the name and value for T2-T1 into the Journal. To use these functions:

    • Place the cursors at the locations used to measure the reaction time.

    • Transfer the name of the T2-T1 function to the Journal using the Add Title to Journal function in the Reaction Time Channel pull-down menu.

    • Transfer the value for T2-T1 to the Journal using the Add Ch. Data to Journal function in the Reaction Time Channel pull-down menu.

6. Once the reflex conduction time in the first trial is measured and recorded, use the scroll bar at the bottom of the Analysis window to move the data from the second trial onto the window. If needed, use the Display Time icons to adjust the width of the Analysis window to show both the signal from the tendon tap and the subject's EMG response on the same window.

7. Use the same techniques used in Steps 5 and 6 to measure the reflex conduction times from the other eight trials.

8. Once the reaction times in all ten trials have been measured and recorded, open the Journal and use the values to determine the mean reflex conduction time of the subject. Discard the longest and shortest times from the data set, and determine the average of the eight remaining reaction times. Convert time to miliseconds. Record the mean reflex conduction time in miliseconds for the patellar reflex for the various experimental conditions in the table that appears in the lab worksheet.

9. Measure the distance between the belly of the subject's quadriceps muscle and the site of the sensory-motor synapse in the spinal cord in millimeters. For the purpose of this exercise, assume that the sensory-motor synapse is at spinal segments L5 and S1, which are just above the top of the hip bone. Multiply this measurement by 2 to determine the total length of the nerve path in millimeters.

10. Even though this stretch reflex is known as a monosynaptic reflex, the pathway includes the neuromuscular synapse (NMJ) as well. Assume that synaptic transmission takes about 0.5 msec, calculate the conduction velocity in the nerves composing this reflex pathway by the equation

$$\text{Conduction velocity (m/sec)} = \frac{\text{Total path length (mm)}}{(\text{Mean reflex time (msec)} - 0.5 \text{ msec})}$$

11. Record the conduction velocities for the patellar reflex for the various experimental conditions in the table that appears in the lab worksheet.

II. Pupillary reflex

The pupillary light reflex and the consensual reflex will be tested in this lab. In both these reflexes the retina of the eye is the sensory receptor, the optic nerve is the sensory neuron, the oculomotor nerve is the motor neuron and the smooth muscles of the iris, the effector. Absence of these reflexes indicates trauma or damage to brain stem. The response observed on one side of the body when the opposite side has been stimulated is called contralateral response and the reflex occurring on the same side as that of the stimulus is called as ipsilateral response.

1. Perform this exercise in a dimly lit area so it does not affect the results of your test. Have a flashlight ready before you start the test.

2. Using the metric ruler measure and record the size of the subject's pupil.

3. Using a paper or the hand vertically as a shield between the two eyes, shine a light into the subject's left eye. The examiner must be standing to the left of the subject to conduct the test.

4. Observe the response of the pupil.

5. Observe the right pupil. Has similar change (consensual response) occurred in the right eye?

Checklist

A. Cross section spinal cord

_____ structures in gray matter (horns)   _____ dorsal root

_____ structures in white matter (funiculi)   _____ ventral root

_____ central canal   _____ dorsal ramus

_____ gray commissure   _____ ventral ramus

_____ dorsal root ganglion   _____ anterior median fissure

_____ posterior median sulcus

B. Plexuses

_____ cervical plexus   _____ phrenic nerve

_____ brachial plexus   _____ ulnar nerve

_____ musculocutaneous nerve   _____ radial nerve

_____ median nerve   _____ axillary nerve

_____ lumbar plexus   _____ femoral nerve

_____ obturator nerve   _____ sacral plexus

_____ sciatic nerve   _____ tibial nerve

_____ peroneal nerve (fibular)

C.   _____ **Reflex**   _____ **reflex arc**

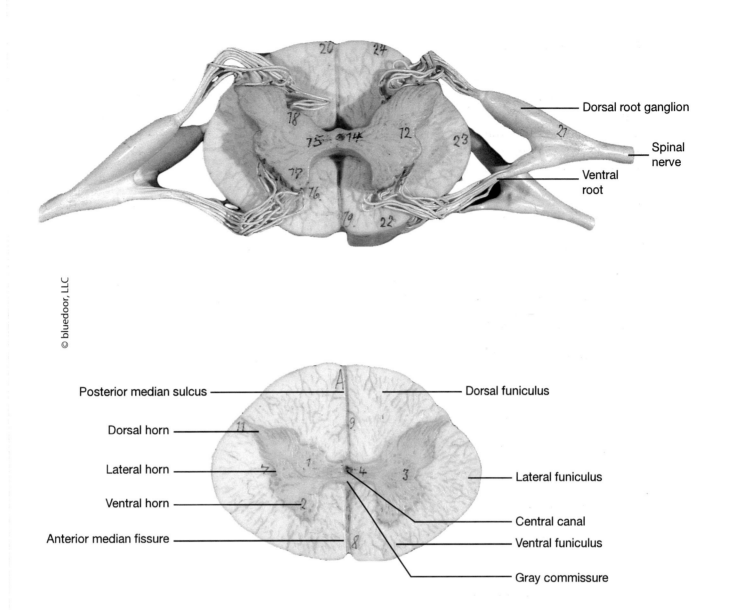

Figure 11.1: Spinal cord, cross-sectional view

Name: _____

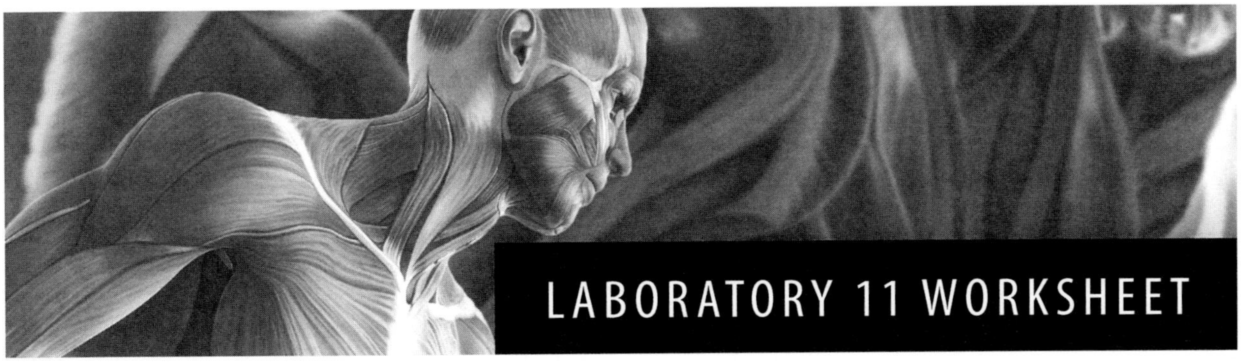

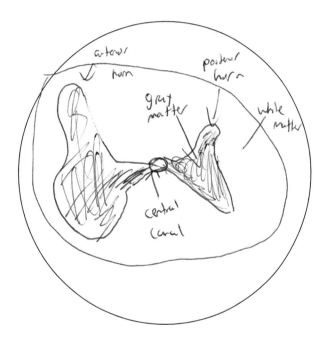

LABORATORY 11 WORKSHEET

LAB 11 WORKSHEET

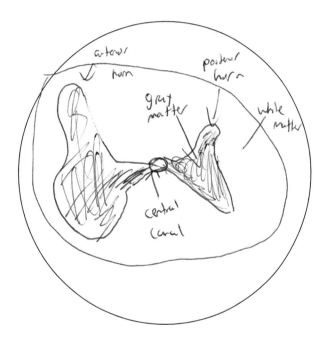

Spinal cord cross section

Total Magnification: _____40x_____

Label the white matter, central canal, anterior median fissure,
posterior median sulcus, posterior horn, anterior horn, gray commisure

(handwritten labels: anterior horn, posterior horn, gray matter, white matter, central canal)

2. Correctly label the diagram using the terms below:

gray matter   white matter   spinal nerve   ventral ramus

dorsal ramus   gray commisure   dorsal root   ventral root

dorsal root ganglion

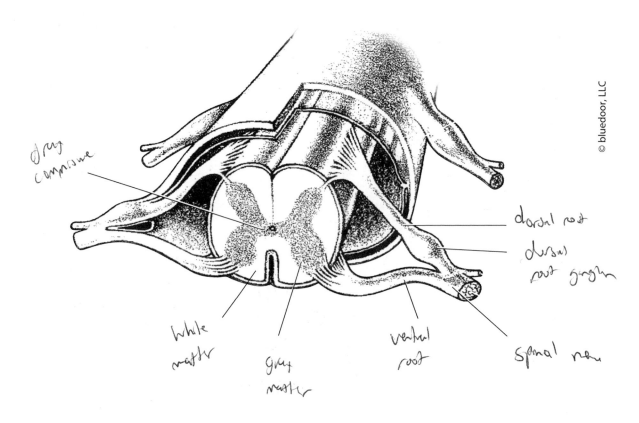

Handwritten labels: gray commisure, dorsal root, dorsal root ganglion, white matter, gray matter, ventral root, spinal nerve

© bluedoor, LLC

3. Reflex Physiology

What are the five essential components of the reflex arc?

| receptor | integration center | sensory neuron |
| motor neuron | effector | stimulus |

4. Stretch reflex (patellar reflex):

Trace the patellar reflex arc, naming receptor, afferent nerve, integration center, efferent nerve, and effector (the specific muscle for the patellar reflex).

receptor – ~~muscle~~ patellar ligament   efferent nerve – motor ~~neuro~~ neuron

afferent nerve – ~~muscle spindle~~ sensory nerve   effector – inner nerves

integration center – spinal cord

5. Pupillary reflex

1. Name the branch of the autonomic nervous system responsible for the pupillary light reflex.

   Sympathetic

2. Describe the protective aspect of the pupillary light reflex.

   The pupil contracts in order to control the amount of light let in.

3. Was the pupillary consensual reflex contralateral or ipsilateral?

   ~~the~~ ~~ipsilateral~~ Contralateral

4. Why would a contralateral response of the pupillary light reflex be of significant value?

   Because it controls the amount of light let through

6. Data tables for patellar reflex

Condition	Mean Reflex Conduction Velocity (m/s)
Patellar reflex	36.84 m/s
Patellar reflex-mental distraction	31.82 m/s

1. Referring back to your results on patellar reflex testing, did mental distraction increase, decrease or have no change on reflex velocity?

   Increase reflex velocity

2. Mental distraction should have increased the conduction velocity of the patellar reflex. Given this information do you think the brain has any influence on spinal reflexes?

   Yes, it does,

POST LAB WORKSHEET LAB 12

1. Using the terms below, label the diagram correctly.

   gray matter   white matter   spinal nerve   ventral ramus

   dorsal ramus   gray commisure   dorsal root   ventral root

   dorsal root ganglion

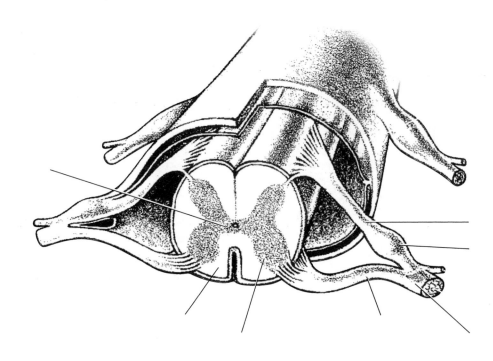

2. Where in the vertebral column is a lumbar puncture normally done in an adult?

   _____

3. Why is this the site of choice?

   _____

4. In what two regions is the spinal cord enlarged?

   _____ and _____

5. What is the significance of these enlargements?

   _____

6. Put these structures in the order in which a sensory signal might pass through, starting with the receptor and ending at the spinal cord:

    dorsal root ganglion   posterior gray horn   ventral ramus

    cervical plexus   spinal nerve C2   lesser occipital nerve

    Receptor, _____, _____, _____,

    _____, _____, _____, spinal cord.

7. How does the location of gray matter and white matter differ in the cerebrum and spinal cord?

    _____

8. List in order (beginning at the spinal cord) the formation of a spinal nerve to the ventral ramus using the following structures:

    dorsal ramus   common spinal nerve   ventral root

    dorsal root ganglion

    Spinal cord, dorsal root, _____, _____, _____,

    _____, ventral ramus.

9. Indicate whether the following components of a spinal nerve are sensory only, motor only, or both.

    Dorsal ramus   _____

    Common spinal nerve   _____

    Ventral root   _____

    Dorsal root ganglion   _____

    Dorsal root   _____

    Ventral ramus   _____

    Musculocutaneous nerve   _____

10. What is a nerve plexus? _____

    _____

    _____

11. The ventral rami of T1 through T12 run between the ribs to serve which muscles?

    _____

12. Referring to the information contained in your textbook, name the major nerves (or nerve plexus) that serve the following:

skin of the neck (plexus)

_____

adductor muscles of the thigh (nerve)

_____

abdominal wall (plexus)

_____

posterior thigh (nerve)

_____

skin of the shoulder (2 plexuses)

_____

_____

diaphragm (nerve)

_____

anterior thigh (nerve)

_____

skin of the lateral 2/3rds of the hand (nerve)

_____

Objectives

1. Identify the structures of the human eye, using diagrams, models and charts available in the laboratory:

lacrimal sac	lacrimal gland
nasolacrimal duct	conjunctiva
sensory tunic (retina)	canal of Schlemm
posterior segment	vitreous body
eyelids (palpebrae)	optic disc
eyelashes	suspensory ligaments
macula lutea	optic nerve
fovea centralis	lens

    anterior segment (aqueous humor, anterior chamber, posterior chamber)
    fibrous tunic: sclera, cornea
    vascular tunic (uvea): ciliary body, ciliary process, iris, pupil, choroid
    extrinsic eye muscles: superior rectus, inferior rectus, medial rectus, lateral rectus, superior oblique, inferior oblique

2. Complete a dissection of a cow eye and identify the following structures:

optic nerve	extrinsic eye muscles
vitreous body	conjunctiva
fibrous tunic (cornea, sclera)	lens
sensory tunic (retina)	vascular tunic (uvea): ciliary body, iris, pupil, choroid

3. Complete the following tests/experiments related to vision: astigmatism, accommodation, color vision, blind spot

4. Identify the pigmented epithelial layer and the neural layer of the retina using a prepared slide, diagram or model; identify what types of cells are found in each layer

5. Identify the following structures of the human ear using diagrams, models and charts available in the laboratory:

external ear:	auricle (pinna), external auditory canal, tympanic membrane
middle ear:	ossicles (malleus, incus, stapes), oval window, auditory (pharyngotympanic) tube
inner ear:	osseous (bony) labyrinth, perilymph, membranous labyrinth, endolymph, cochlea, vestibule, round window, semicircular canals, vestibulocochlear (auditory) nerve, cochlear duct, scala vestibuli, scala tympani, organ of Corti

6. Identify the following structures of the inner ear using a prepared slide, diagram or model: vestibular membrane, scala vestibuli, cochlear duct, organ of Corti, scala tympani, osseous labyrinth, basilar membrane, hair cells, tectorial membrane, membranous labyrinth

INTRODUCTION:

Hearing and vision are two of the five special senses; the others are taste (gustatory sense), olfaction (smell), and equilibrium. This lab will examine the structure and function of the ear and the eye, which act as receptors for the sensation of vision and hearing.

ACTIVITY 1:

Anatomy of the Human Eye

Materials:

Models and charts of the human eye

Resources: Textbook: pages 545-553

Identify the following structures on diagrams, charts and models of the human eye. Refer to the suggested pages in your textbook:

lacrimal sac	lacrimal gland
nasolacrimal duct	conjunctiva
sensory tunic (retina)	canal of Schlemm
posterior segment	vitreous body
eyelids (palpebrae)	optic disc
eyelashes	suspensory ligaments
macula lutea	optic nerve
fovea centralis	lens

anterior segment (aqueous humor, anterior chamber, posterior chamber)
fibrous tunic: sclera, cornea
vascular tunic (uvea): ciliary body, ciliary process, iris, pupil, choroid
extrinsic eye muscles: superior rectus, inferior rectus, medial rectus, lateral rectus, superior oblique, inferior oblique

ACTIVITY 2:

Eye Dissection

Materials:

    dissecting pan

    preserved eye

    dissecting tools: forceps, scalpel, dissecting scissors, blunt probe, teasing needle

    gloves

    goggles

Follow the directions below and locate the indicated structures:

1.   Trim away the adipose tissue from the surface of the eye, leaving the optic nerve and extrinsic eye muscles intact.

2.   Locate the following structures on the external aspect of the eye:

Extrinsic Eye Muscles:	six skeletal muscles attached in various locations to the surface of the eye
Conjunctiva:	thin, mucous membrane over the anterior surface of the eye, that lines the inner eyelid
Sclera:	the white, fibrous outer tunic (coat) of the eye
Cornea:	the clear, anterior portion of the outer tunic (coat)
Iris:	the pigmented region beneath the cornea
Pupil:	the central opening in the iris (it may be oblong shaped in the specimen)

  Optic nerve: nerve bundle that projects from the posterior surface of the eye

3.   Puncture the sclera with the tip of your dissecting scissors, about 1 cm posterior to the cornea. Use the scissors to cut a circle around the eye, about 1 cm away from the edge of the cornea. Carefully remove the anterior portion away from the posterior portion. Identify these features:

Vitreous humor:	thick fluid that occupies the **posterior segment**
Aqueous humor:	a watery liquid in the posterior chamber of the **anterior segment**
Lens:	a ball of translucent tissue
Ciliary body:	a ring of ridges around the outside of the iris' margin (the ridges are formed by the ciliary muscle)
Retina:	a thin film of gray matter loosely associated with the inside posterior wall of the eyeball; it is attached at the **optic disc**

Choroid: the pigmented region of the **vascular tunic** of the eye, deep to the sclera, superficial to the retina. In some mammals (not humans) an iridescent **tapetum lucidum** is present in the choroid.

ACTIVITY 3:

Tests of Visual Function

Materials:

Meter stick

Straight pin

Ishihara's Color Plates

Resources: Textbook: pages page 554-560

Perform the following tests of visual function and record your observations on the lab worksheet.

A. Astigmatism is an abnormal curvature in the lens or the cornea that can lead to blurred vision.

1. View the astigmatism chart at a distance of about 1 meter.

2. Cover one eye and stare at the center of the astigmatism chart. All of the lines should appear straight and of equal darkness. If any of them are wavy, curved or blurred, some degree of astigmatism is present.

3. Repeat the test using the other eye.

B. **Accommodation** is the ability to adjust the eye's focusing apparatus to account for changes in distance from the object being viewed.

Near point accommodation: The lens becomes rounded (more convex) when viewing close objects. This change in the shape of the lens requires lens elasticity. Lens elasticity can be tested by measuring the near point of accommodation. The normal value in young adults in 10 cm; it is closer in children and farther in older individuals.

1. Hold a straight pin at a distance of 1 meter in front of one eye. Slowly move the pin towards that eye and record the nearest distance at which the pin is clearly visible (not distorted) – this is that eye's near point. Record that distance.

2. Repeat process with the other eye, and record the near point.

C. **Accommodation pupillary reflex:** The pupil changes size to accommodate for the distance of viewed objects.

1. The subject should focus on a distant object in the room (anything but a light) for about 1 minute. Observe the subject's pupils.

2. Hold some printed material about 25 cm (10 inches) away from the subject's face and direct him/her to focus on it. Note any change in the size of the pupils as they focus on this near object.

D. **Blind Spot:** There are no photoreceptors in the optic disc and image points focused there cannot be visualized. Follow these steps to demonstrate the location of the blind spot in a subject's visual field.

1. Hold the figure below about 46 cm (18 inches) away from the eyes.

2. Close the left eye and align the "X" in the image with the right eye. Slowly move the figure closer, keeping the right eye focused on the "X". When the "dot" focuses on the blind spot, it will disappear. The dot will reappear when the figure is moved nearer. Record the distance where the dot disappears.

3. Repeat this procedure for the left eye.

E. **Color Blindness:** Defects in the color photoreceptor cells (cones) can lead to color vision deficiencies. These defects are tested for using Ishihara's color plates.

1. View the color plates in bright light at a distance of about 75 cm. Record what you see in each plate (make a decision within 5 seconds) and check for accuracy against information provided in the book.

2. Record your observation for each plate in the worksheet.

ACTIVITY 4:

Microscopic Anatomy of the Retina

Materials:

Microscope

Lens Cleaner

Lens Paper

Prepared Slide – Longitudinal Section of the Eye

Resources: Textbook: pages 549-551

Observe the retina and identify the following: pigmented epithelial layer, outer segments of rods and cones, ganglion cells, nuclei of rods and cones, nuclei of bipolar cells, neural layer.

ACTIVITY 5:

Anatomy of the Human Ear

Materials:

Charts and models of the human ear

Resources: Textbook: pages 570-575

Identify the following structures of the human ear using diagrams, models and charts available in the laboratory. Refer to the suggested pages in your textbook.

External ear:	auricle (pinna), external auditory canal, tympanic membrane
Middle ear:	ossicles (malleus, incus, stapes), oval window, auditory (pharyngotympanic) tube
Inner ear:	osseous (bony) labyrinth, perilymph, membranous labyrinth, endolymph, cochlea, vestibule, round window, semicircular canals, vestibulocochlear (auditory) nerve, cochlear duct, scala vestibuli, scala tympani, organ of Corti

ACTIVITY 6:

Microscopic Structure of the Cochlea

Materials:

Microscope, lens cleaner, lens paper, prepared slide - cochlea

Resources: Textbook: page 574

Identify the following structures of the inner ear using a prepared slide, diagram or model: vestibular membrane, scala vestibuli, cochlear duct, organ of Corti, scala tympani, osseous labyrinth, basilar membrane, hairs cells, tectorial membrane, membranous labyrinth

Checklist:

Activity 1 and 2: Eye Anatomy

Tunic or Region	Structure	Human	Animal
Lacrimal Apparatus	Lacrimal gland Nasolacrimal duct		X X
Extrinsic Eye Muscles	Rectus, superior, Inferior, lateral, medial		
External Accessories	Conjunctiva Eyelids, Eyebrows		X X
Outer Coat	Cornea Sclera		
Middle Coat	Choroid Ciliary Body Lens Suspensory Ligaments Iris Pupil Tapetum Lucidum (cow eye only)	X	
Inner Coat	Retina Optic Disc Macula Lutea		X
Anterior Cavity	Aqueous Humor		
Posterior Cavity	Vitreous Humor Optic Nerve		

Activity 3: Visual Tests

_____ Astigmatism   _____ Blind Spot

_____ Near Point Accommodation   _____ Color Blindness

Activity 4: Microscopic Anatomy of the Retina

_____ pigmented epithelial layer

_____ neural layer

_____ outer segments of rods and cones

_____ retinal ganglion cells

_____ nuclei of rods and cones

Activity 5: Structures of the Human Ear:

External Ear	Middle Ear	Inner Ear
___ auricle (pinna)	___ ossicles ___ malleus ___ incus ___ stapes	___ osseous (bony) labyrinth ___ perilymph
___ external auditory canal	___ oval window	___ membranous labyrinth ___ endolymph
___ tympanic membrane	___ auditory (pharyngotympanic) tube	___ cochlea ___ cochlear duct ___ scala vestibule ___ scala tympani ___ round window ___ organ of Corti
		___ semicircular canals
		___ vestibule (utricle and saccule)

Activity 6: Microscopic Structure of the Cochlea

_____ Vestibular membrane

_____ Scala vestibuli

_____ Cochlear duct

_____ Organ of Corti

_____ Hair cells

_____ Scala tympani

_____ Osseous labyrinth

_____ Membranous labyrinth

_____ Basilar membrane

_____ Tectorial membrane

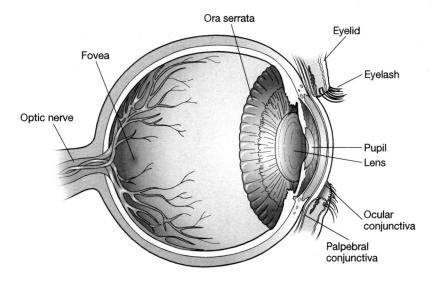

Sagittal section of left eye

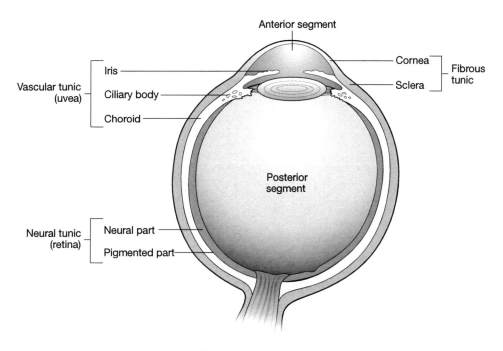

Horizontal section of right eye

Figure 12.1: Structure of the eye

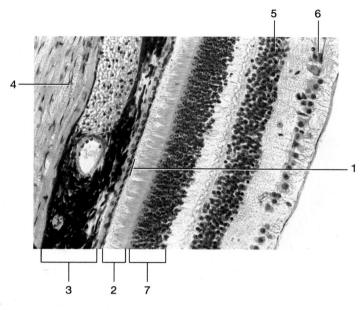

Figure 12.2: Retina. 1) Retina 2) Rods and cones
3) Choroid 4) Sclera 5) Bipolar cell nuclei
6) Retinal ganglion cell layer 7) nuclei of rods and cones

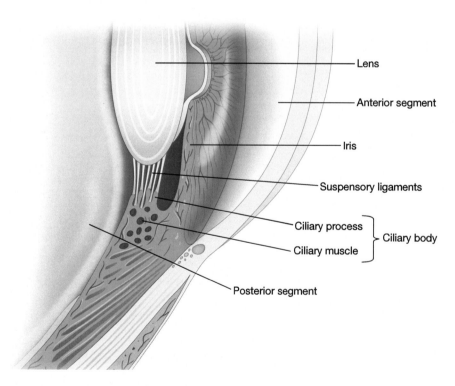

Figure 12.3: Anterior portion of the eye.

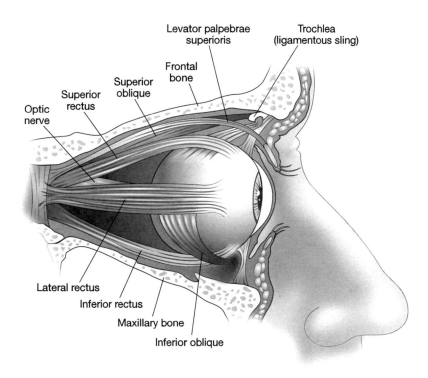

Lateral surface, right eye

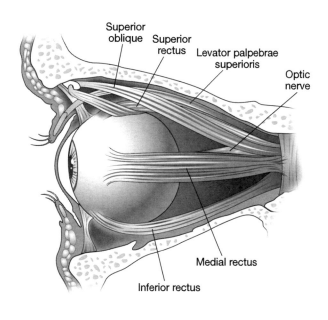

Medial surface, right eye

Figure 12.4: Eye, lateral and medial views

© bluedoor, LLC

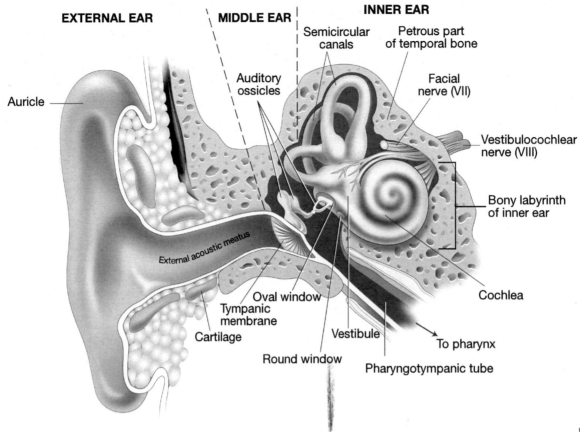

EXTERNAL EAR

MIDDLE EAR

INNER EAR

Semicircular canals

Petrous part of temporal bone

Auditory ossicles

Facial nerve (VII)

Auricle

Vestibulocochlear nerve (VIII)

Bony labyrinth of inner ear

External acoustic meatus

Oval window

Tympanic membrane

Cartilage

Vestibule

Cochlea

Round window

To pharynx

Pharyngotympanic tube

Figure 12.5: Human ear

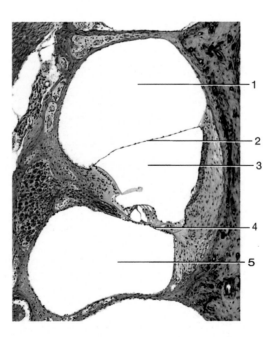

Figure 12.6: Cochlea. 1) Scala vestibuli
2) Vestibular membrane 3) Cochlear duct
4) Basilar membrane 5) Scala tympani

Name:

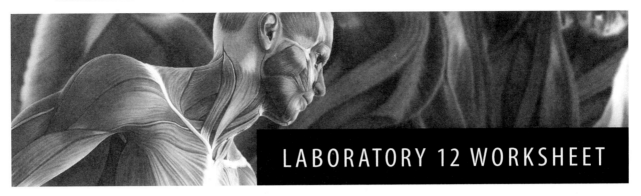

LAB 12 WORKSHEET

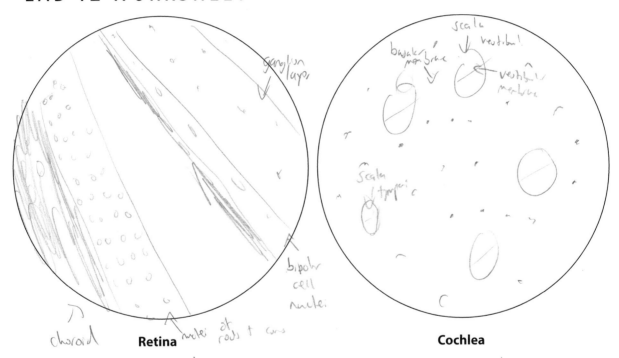

Retina

Total Magnification: _____
Label the ganglion cell layer,
bipolar cell nuclei, nuclei of the
rods and cones, choroid

Cochlea

Total Magnification: _____
Label the scala vestibuli, vestibular
membrane, scala media, tectorial
membrane, spiral organ of Corti,
basilar membrane, scala tympani

1. **Astigmatism:**

   Define the term "astigmatism" _Defect of the lens where the_
   cornea or lens is irregularly shaped

   How can astigmatism be corrected? _Through contacts or LASIK surgery_

Is astigmatism present in the right eye? _No_____

Is astigmatism present in the left eye? _No_____

2. Accommodation:

Near point accommodation distance (cm) right eye: _11 cr_____

Near point accommodation distance (cm) left eye: _~~10~~ cr_____

Is your near point within the normal range for your age? _____

What happened to the size of the pupil when it was exposed to light?

_The size of the pupil decreases,_____

What muscle constricts to cause this change? _ciliary_ ~~muscle~~ _muscle_

3. Color Blindness

Record your results for the color blindness test in the table below:

Plate Number	Image Observed
12	9 7

What is the usual cause of color blindness? _~~Sex linked~~ X-linked trait_

_____

4. Blind Spot:

Blind spot distance, right eye: _____

Blind spot distance, left eye: _____

Explain why vision is lost when light hits the blind spot: _Because it is not_

rentored by the sclera

_____

POST LAB WORKSHEET LAB 13

1. Match the following parts of the eye to their function:

   ciliary body, sclera, iris, retina, lens, pupil, & tapetum lucidum

   _____ Contains the photoreceptors for vision.

   _____ The colored portion of the eye.

   _____ This structure changes shape to focus light on the retina.

   _____ The opening in the iris through which light passes.

   _____ The iridescent portion of the choroid layer found in nocturnal
   animals.

   _____ Consists of muscles, which control and shape the lens.

   _____ The white of the eye.

2. Match the parts of the ear to their function:

   ossicles, auricle (pinna), round window, tympanic membrane, perilymph, semicircular canals,
   membranous labyrinth, cochlear duct

   _____ The vestibular membrane and the basilar membrane are walls of the?

   _____ The most external portion of the external ear.

   _____ Contains receptors for the sense of balance.

   _____ Fluid contained within the bony labyrinth.

   _____ The malleus, incus and stapes.

   _____ Involved in equalizing pressure between the external and middle ear.

   _____ Dissipates fluid pressure in the scala tympani; bulges into the
   tympanic cavity.

3. Label the diagram of the eye:

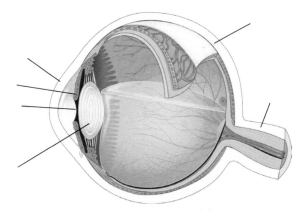 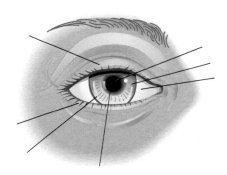

4. You would expect the pupil to be dilated in which of the following circumstances (Place a check next to the correct responses):

_____ in brightly lit surroundings _____ during focusing on near objects

_____ in dimly lit surroundings _____ during focusing on distant objects

5. Indicate whether each of the following statements refers to rods (r), cones (c), or both (b)

_____ Located in the neural layer of the retina

_____ Absent in the optic disc

_____ Are bright light, high discrimination receptors

_____ Are low light intensity receptors; used for peripheral vision and night vision

_____ Are scattered over the periphery of the retina

_____ Are concentrated in the fovea centralis

_____ Contain the visual pigment rhodopsin

_____ There are three types: red, green and blue

6. Label the structures on the diagram using the following list:

Auricle (pinna)	external acoustic meatus	tympanic membrane
Malleus	incus	stapes
Temporal bone	semicircular canals	vestibulocochlear nerve
Cochlea	vestibule	

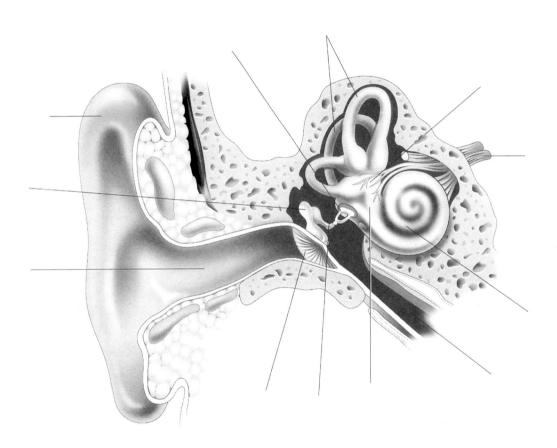

7. Sound waves hitting the eardrum initiate its vibratory motion. Trace the pathway through which vibrations and fluid currents are transmitted to finally stimulate the organ of Corti, beginning with the eardrum:

Eardrum _____

_____

_____

_____

8. What is the difference between static equilibrium and dynamic equilibrium? What inner ear structures are responsible for each of these? Complete the chart below:

	Static Equilibrium	Dynamic Equilibrium
Definition		
Structures Involved		

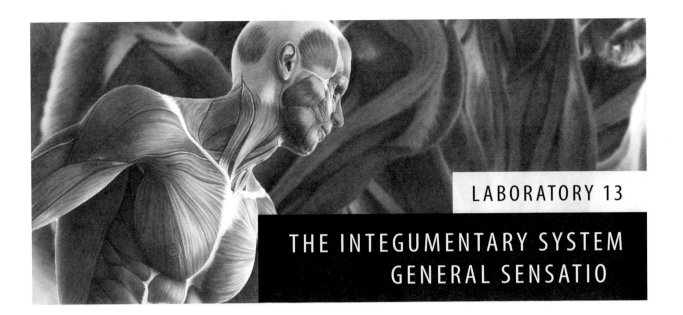

Objectives

1. Identify the following structures associated with the integument using a diagram, model or prepared slide:

epidermis	dermis	hypodermis
stratum corneum	papillary layer	reticular layer
stratum lucidum	dermal papilla	Meissner's corpuscle
stratum granulosum	free nerve ending	sebaceous gland
stratum spinosum	suderiferous gland	arrector pili muscle
stratum basale	hair follicle	root hair plexus
hair root	hair shaft	hair papilla
hair bulb	hair matrix	keratinocyte
melanocyte	epithelial root sheath	connective tissue root sheath
Pacinian Corpuscle		

2. Collect and analyze data for the experiments which investigate the properties of somatic sensory receptors.

INTRODUCTION

The integumentary system consists of the skin and its derivatives (hair, nails, and glands). The skin is an epithelial membrane, composed of a superficial layer of keratinized stratified squamous epithelium (epidermis) and a deeper layer of connective tissue (dermis). The hypodermis (subcutaneous tissue, superficial fascia), composed of connective tissue, attaches the skin to underlying structures, but is not considered to be part of the skin.

The functions of the integumentary system include protection, regulation of body temperature, excretion of wastes, synthesis of vitamin D and sensory reception. Free nerve endings and encapsulated nerve endings in the skin detect a variety of sensory modalities, including pain (nociceptors), touch and pressure (mechanoreceptors), heat or cold (thermoreceptors), and even itching. The acuteness of the sensation depends on the density of the receptors while the modality (type) and location of each sensation is determined by the specific sensory pathway and sensory processing in the brain.

Physiologists have traditionally believed that each sensation is mediated by a different sensory receptor, a view supported by the histological identification of distinct cutaneous receptors. Mapping experiments have revealed that these receptors are not generalized throughout the skin, but are clustered at certain points (punctate distribution).

Adaptation is a decline in the activity of sensory receptors that may occur over time due to constantly maintained stimulation. Fast adapting, or phasic receptors, respond immediately when a stimulus is applied but the response can disappear if the stimulus is maintained long enough. Slow adapting, or tonic receptors, respond to a sustained stimulus with an initial increase in activity that decays to a smaller increase which is maintained for as long as the stimulus lasts.

This laboratory exercise provides an introduction to the structures of the integumentary system and includes experiments that can be used to investigate the location and physiology of cutaneous receptors.

Materials

1. Each student should have a compound microscope

2. Each pair of students should have:

    Lens paper

    Lens cleaner

    Box of prepared slides: thick skin, thin skin with hair, skin (corpuscle), Vater-Pacini Corpuscle

    Colored pencils

3. Class materials to be shared by students:

    Three dimensional models of the integument

    Charts of the integumentary system

ACTIVITY 1

Integumentary System – Anatomy

Resources: Textbook: pages 152 – 162

1. Examine the charts and three dimensional models of the integumentary system and identify:

epidermis	dermis	hypodermis
stratum corneum	papillary layer	reticular layer
stratum lucidum	dermal papilla	Meissner's corpuscle
stratum granulosum	free nerve ending	sebaceous gland
stratum spinosum	sudoriferous gland	arrector pili muscle
stratum basale	hair follicle	root hair plexus
hair root	hair shaft	hair papilla
hair bulb	hair matrix	keratinocyte
melanocyte	epithelial root sheath	connective tissue root sheath
Pacinian Corpuscle		

2. Examine the following prepared slides under the microscope and prepare labeled sketches of each one. Be sure to look at the label to determine whether the tissue has been sectioned transversely or longitudinally.

A. Thin Human Skin

epidermis: observe the stratum basale, the stratum spinosum, the stratum granulosum and the stratum corneum; compare the shapes of the keratinocyte, in each layer and the presence/absence of nuclei and granules

dermis: observe the papillary layer and dermal papillae (areolar connective tissue) and reticular layer (dense irregular connective tissue); you should be able to differentiate between the thin mesh-like papillary layer and the thicker reticular layer with its network of dense coarse collagen fibers, also look for eccrine sweat glands

hypodermis: also called subcutaneous tissue or superficial fascia, it consists of adipose tissue and areolar connective tissue

B. Thin, Pigmented Human Skin

Observe the same structures as those above, but look now for melanin granules in the keratinocytes located in the deeper epidermal layers

C. Thick Skin: Palmar or Plantar Skin

Observe the same structure as in thin skin, but note the different appearance of the epidermis which now includes a stratum lucidum and a thicker stratum corneum; you may see many eccrine sweat (sudoriferous) glands on this slide.

D. Hairy Skin (Monkey or Human Scalp)

Observe the same structures as in thin skin, but also observe hair follicles, arrector pili muscle, hair (shaft, root), hair bulb, hair papilla, and sebaceous glands.

Tips:

1. Most hair follicles will be cut at odd angles and only a few good longitudinally- or transversely-cut profiles are visible.

2. The hair may have been lost during the preparation of the specimen and not all hair follicles will contain hairs.

3. Although it is often possible to see the attachment of the arrector pili muscle into the hair follicle or the papillary layer of the dermis, both attachments are hardly ever visible in the same section.

E. Meissner's (Tactile) Corpuscle

Locate a tactile corpuscle in a dermal papilla. This is an oval, encapsulated touch receptor composed of flattened connective tissue stacked horizontally and a sensory nerve fiber.

F. Pacinian (Lamellated) Corpuscle

Locate a lamellated corpuscle in the deep portions of the dermis or in subcutaneous tissue. These are large onion-shaped receptors composed of a central nerve ending surrounded by several concentric layers of connective tissue

ACTIVITY 2:

General Sensation

Materials:

Each pair of students should have:

Mall Probes

Small Metric Ruler

Non-toxic, Washable, Fine-Pointed Markers (Black, Red, Blue)

Caliper or Compass

Von Frey's Hairs or Horse Hair

Beaker of Ice Water, Chipped Ice

Access to a Hot Water Bath (45°C)

Laboratory Thermometer

Stopwatch

One Five-Gram Weight and One Ten-Gram Weight

Three Large Finger Bowls or 1000 ml Beakers

Resources: Textbook: pages 491-495

Complete the activities below with your lab partner:

A. Two- Point Discrimination Test

The relative density of touch receptors in the skin can be determined by performing a two-point discrimination test. Using a compass or caliper and a metric ruler, you will touch a subject's skin simultaneously at two points and determine the minimum distance at which the points can be perceived as two, rather than as one, sensation.

1. Adjust the compass or caliper so that its two points are touching.

2. With your partner's eyes closed and hand placed palm upward, on the lab table, gently place the compass (caliper) points simultaneously on the surface of your partner's index finger. **Do not press hard. Pressing hard will produce inaccurate results and may harm the subject.**

3. Move the points apart by about 1 mm and touch the finger again.

4. Repeat this sequence, increasing the distance slightly, until your partner tells you that two distinct points are perceived. Record the distance between the points at this time in the lab worksheet.

5. Repeat the test for the following areas: face, posterior surface of the hand, palmar surface, posterior neck, ventral forearm, and posterior forearm.

B. Mapping Temperature and Touch Receptors

In this experiment you will compare the density of cold, heat and touch receptors in a single area of skin.

1. Place one Mall probe in a beaker of ice water and another in a 45°C water bath. Let the probes reach the temperature of each respective bath (this should take a few minutes) before using them.

2. With a washable felt marker, draw a square (2 cm per side) on the ventral forearm of the subject. Using a ruler, subdivide the square into 16 blocks by drawing a grid within the box (use a ruler).

3. With the subject's eyes closed, touch the tip of a horsehair (or Von Frey's hair) to a point on the grid just hard enough to bend the hair slightly. Mark the position with a black dot if it is perceived. Touch all sixteen locations in the square in this manner, placing a black dot where the touch is perceived. Record your results in the lab worksheet.

   Hint: Touch the subject at random intervals and in a random pattern to avoid anticipation on the part of the subject that might alter your results.

4. Remove the probe from the ice water bath and wipe it dry with a towel. Repeat the procedure outlined above marking each point of cold perception with a blue dot. Make sure that the subject is perceiving cold, not touch. The probe needs to be returned to the ice water bath every two minutes to maintain the desired temperature. Record your results on the lab worksheet.

5. Remove the probe from the 45°C water bath and repeat the procedure again, this time marking all points of heat perception with a red dot. Make sure that the subject perceives heat, not touch. Return the probe to the 45°C water bath every two minutes to maintain its temperature. Record your results on the lab worksheet.

C. Tactile Localization

Once the tactile receptor receives a stimulus, the input information must be encoded into an electrical signal and conveyed to the central nervous system. It is within the central nervous system that information must be localized and perceived. The area of the skin monitored by a receptor is called its receptive field. When the receptive field for a particular receptor is small, the brain is able to be more accurate in localizing the stimulus.

1. The subject's eyes should remain closed and their hand should rest on the lab table, palm upward.

2. Touch the subject's palm with a marker of one color, and have the subject try to touch the exact same point with a marker of another color. Measure the distance between the two points (error of localization) in millimeters and record the results on the lab worksheet.

3. Repeat the test in the same spot two additional times, recording the errors of localization for each trial. Then, average the results.

4. Repeat the experiment for the fingertip, ventral forearm, back of the hand and back of the neck.

D. Sensory Adaptation

1. The experimenter should hold a 5-gram weight and a 10-gram weight in your hand until they are warm to the touch.

2. The subject should sit comfortably with their eyes close and forearm extended.

3. Place the 5-gram weight on the anterior surface of the subject's forearm.

4. Determine how long the initial pressure sensation persists in seconds. Record your results on the laboratory worksheet.

5. Repeat the test again at a nearby location on the anterior forearm using a 10-gram weight. Determine how long the initial pressure sensation persists in seconds.

E. Adaptation of Temperature Receptors

These receptors detect relative differences between the temperature of the environment and the inner temperature of the skin. Our perception of temperature is not only dependent on the current temperature, but is also dependent on the previous temperature. Temperature receptors adapt rapidly when presented with new temperature signals.

1. Fill a large beaker or bowl with 45°C water.

The subject should immerse their left hand in the water and note the sensation.

Keep the left hand in the water for one minute and then add the right hand. The subject should note the sensation perceived from the right hand and compare the sensation from the right hand to that of the left hand. Record these observations on the lab worksheet.

Checklist:

A. Skin Histology

_____ Epidermis	_____ Hair Root
_____ Stratum Corneum	_____ Hair Bulb
_____ Stratum Lucidum	_____ Dermal Papilla
_____ Stratum Granulosum	_____ Free Nerve Ending
_____ Stratum Spinosum	_____ Sudoriferous gland
_____ Stratum Basale	_____ Hair Follicle
_____ Keratinocyte	_____ Hair Shaft
_____ Melanocyte	_____ Epithelial Root Sheath
_____ Dermis	_____ Sebaceous Gland
_____ Papillary Layer	_____ Arrector Pili Muscle

_____ Reticular Layer _____ Root Hair Plexus

_____ Hypodermis _____ Hair Papilla

_____ Pacinian Corpuscle _____ Connective Tissue Root Sheath

_____ Meissner's Corpuscle _____ Hair Matrix

B. General Sensation

_____ Two Point Discrimination Test completed

_____ Mapping Temperature and Touch Receptors experiment completed

_____ Tactile Localization experiment completed

_____ Sensory Adaptation experiment completed

_____ Adaptation of Temperature Receptors experiment completed

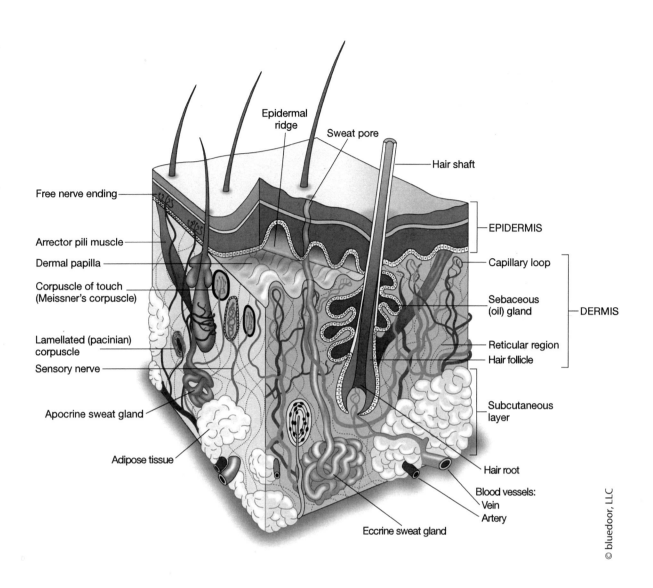

Free nerve ending

Arrector pili muscle

Dermal papilla

Corpuscle of touch
(Meissner's corpuscle)

Lamellated (pacinian)
corpuscle

Sensory nerve

Apocrine sweat gland

Adipose tissue

Epidermal
ridge

Sweat pore

Hair shaft

EPIDERMIS

Capillary loop

Sebaceous
(oil) gland

DERMIS

Reticular region

Hair follicle

Subcutaneous
layer

Hair root

Blood vessels:
Vein
Artery

Eccrine sweat gland

© bluedoor, LLC

Figure 13.1: Human skin, epidermal structures

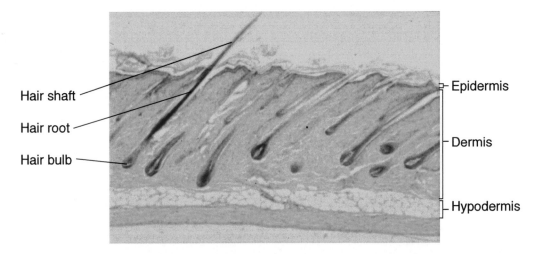

Hair shaft

Hair root

Hair bulb

Epidermis

Dermis

Hypodermis

Figure 13.2: Skin

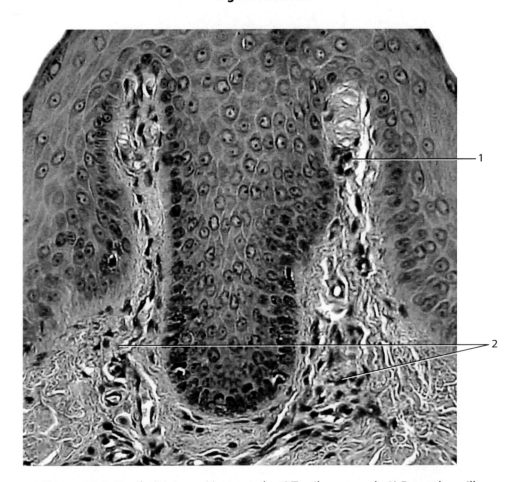

1

2

Figure 13.3: Tactile (Meissner's) corpuscle. 1) Tactile corpuscle 2) Dermal papillae

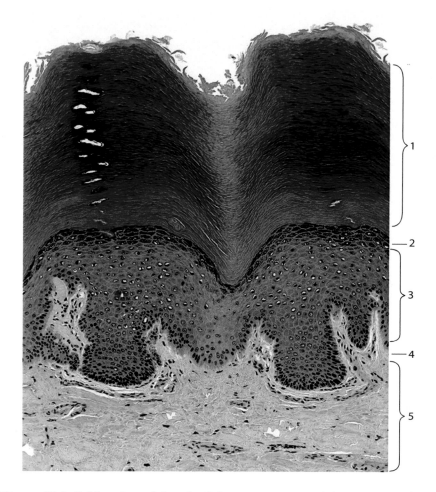

Figure 13.4: Epidermis and dermis. 1) Stratum corneum 2) Stratum granulosum
3) Stratum spinosum 4) Stratum basale 5) Dermis

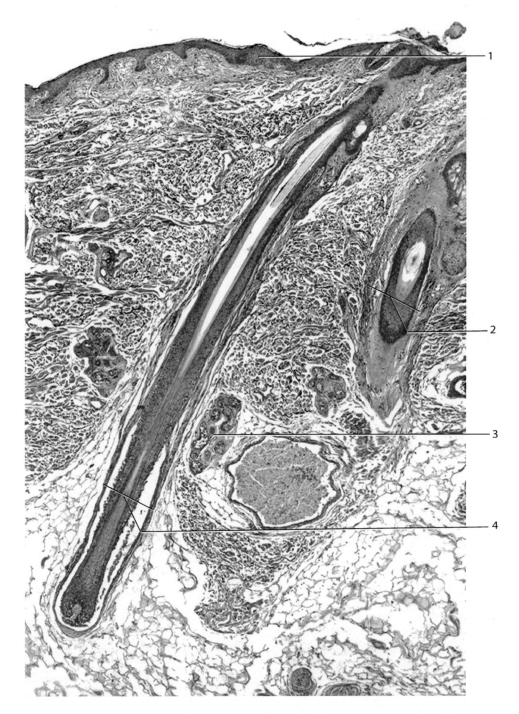

Figure 13.5: Hair follicle. 1) Epidermis 2) Hair follicle (oblique cut)
3) Sebaceous gland 4) Hair follicle

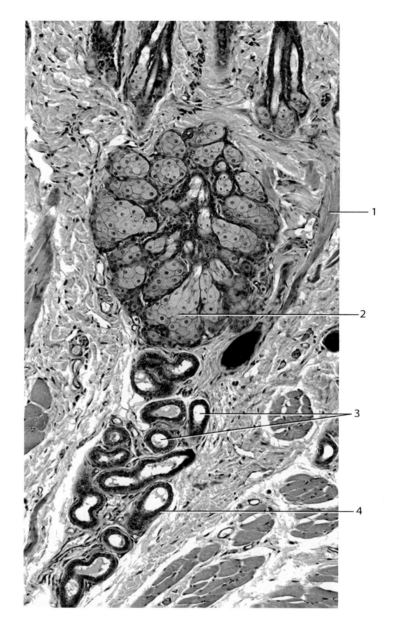

Figure 13.6: 1) Arrector pili muscle 2) Sebaceous gland
3) Excretory portion of sweat gland 4) Secretory portion of sweat gland

Name:_____

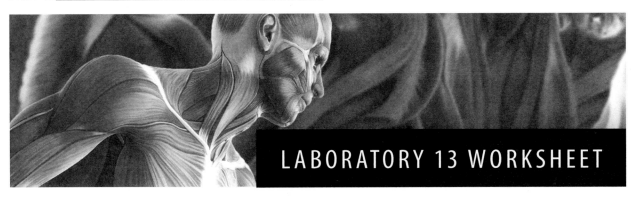

LAB 13 WORKSHEET

Prepare labeled drawings as seen under the microscope

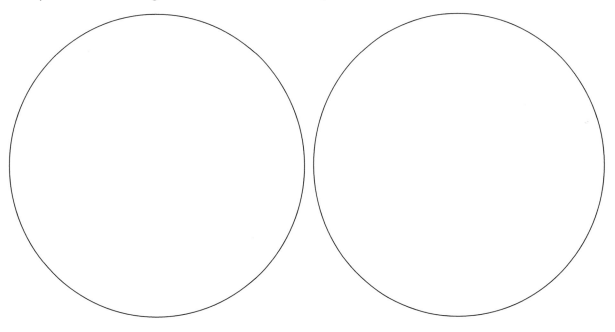

Thin Human Skin

Total magnification: _____
Label the stratum basale,
stratum spinosum, stratum granulosum,
stratum corneum

Dermis

Total magnification: _____
Label the epidermis, papillary layer of the
dermis, dermal papilla, reticular layer
of the dermis, eccrine sweat gland and
Pacinian corpuscle

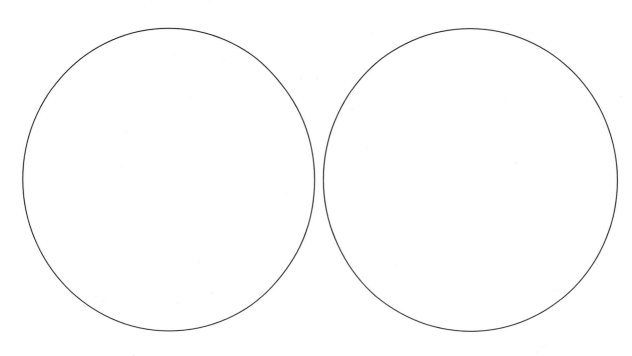

Thick Human Skin

Total magnification: _____
Label stratum basale, stratum spinosum,
stratum granulosum, stratum lucidum,
stratum corneum

Hairy Skin

Total magnification: _____
Label a hair follicle, sebaceous gland,
arrector pili muscle

Data Tables For General Sensation Experiments:

a. Determining Two-Point Threshold

Body Area Tested	Two Point Threshold (mm)
Face	24 mm
Posterior Hand	18 mm
Palm	12 mm
Posterior Neck	70 mm
Ventral Forearm	21 mm
Posterior Forearm	27 mm

b. Mapping Touch and Temperature Receptors

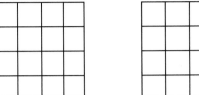

| Touch Receptor | Cold Receptor | Heat Receptor |
| Map | Map | Map |

c. Tactile Localization (Record the Error of Localization)

Body Area Tested	Trial 1 (mm)	Trial 2 (mm)	Trial 3 (mm)	Average (mm)
Palm of Hand	11 mm	10 mm	14 mm	10.67 mm
Fingertip	1 mm	1 mm	2 mm	1.33 mm
Ventral Forearm	16 mm	14 mm	15 mm	15 mm
Back of Hand	4 mm	6 mm	3 mm	4.33 mm
Back of Neck				

d. Sensory Adaptation

Weight	Duration of Pressure Sensation (secs)
5 gram	(8)
10 gram	(3)

e. Adaptation of Temperature Receptors

Sensation after one minute – left hand	
Sensation upon immersion – right hand	

POST LAB WORKSHEET LAB 13

1. Label the diagram below with the letter of the correct term:

    a. Pacinian Corpuscle

    b. sebaceous gland

    c. stratum granulosum

    d. eccrine sweat gland

    e. hair shaft

    f. stratum spinosum

    g. Meissner's Corpuscle

    h. hair follicle

    i. hair papilla

    j. arrector pili muscle

    k. stratum corneum

    l. stratum basale

    m. hypodermis

    n. root hair plexus

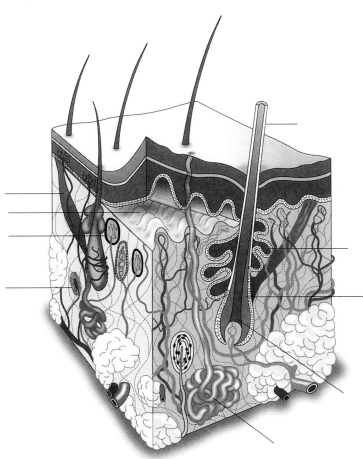

1. Which epidermal strata do you find in thick but not thin skin?

    _____

2. Identify the type of tissue that makes up the:

    Epidermis: _____

    Papillary region (dermis): _____

    Reticular region (dermis): _____

    Hypodermis: _____

3. Provide the correct term for each statement below:

    a. The pigment secreted by a melanocyte: _____

    b. Gland that produces an oily secretion
        that lubricates the hair and skin surface: _____

    c. The waterproofing protein produced
        by keratinocytes: _____

    d. Structures that detect pain and
        temperature sensations: _____

    e. Dermal receptors for light touch: _____

    f. Dermal and hypodermal receptors
        for pressure and vibration: _____

    g. Term for the particular area monitored
        by a single sensory receptor: _____

    h. Term that refers to a decrease in the
        sensitivity of a receptor in the presence
        of constant stimulation: _____